Muck and Magic

DAN CHERRINGTON

MUCK AND MAGIC

with illustrations by
Barry Larking

WHITTET BOOKS

For John and Preston

First published 1991
Text © 1991 by Dan Cherrington
Illustrations © 1991 by Barry Larking
Whittet Books Ltd, 18 Anley Road, London W14 0BY

Design by Paul Minns

All rights reserved

Typeset by Litho Link Ltd, Welshpool, Powys

Printed and bound by Billings and Sons, Worcester

British Library Cataloguing in Publication Data

Cherrington, Dan
Muck and magic.
I. Title
630.92

ISBN 0905483952

CONTENTS

GETTING STARTED

I started off farming on my own with plenty of theory and not much practice. A university degree and two years swanning around the world sounds fine, but it doesn't teach you to milk cows and shear a sheep. When I got back from my world trip, eager to get stuck into some proper farming, there was a council of war. My elder brother Syd was helping Father by this time and the general idea was that he should go off on his own whilst I become Father's No.2. The three of us sat in Father's office.

'Well, Dan, it's nice to have you back; I suppose you're keen to get to work on the farm and learn the ropes?' said Father.

'Too right, Father,' I said. Australia had left its mark. 'But I don't want to upset arrangements between you and Syd.'

Syd and Father got on pretty well together – something I found hard to understand seeing that Father was so old-fashioned in his ideas: perhaps Syd lacked ambition.

'I'd be willing to have a go on my own right away. Er, provided you would help, of course,' I added to Father.

'Really, Dan,' said Syd, 'that would suit me OK. I enjoy farming here and reckon I'm learning a good deal.'

So it was settled and, after a few months frenzied farm hunting, I wound up in the south-west 150 miles or so from home at

Netton Farm. What excitement and what a challenge!

'Dan, your first job will be to find a reliable contractor and arrange to get the spring crops sown.' We had taken the farm on at Christmas and getting some cash crops in the ground was pretty important.

'Righto, Father,' I said, as I prepared to set off in my old van. 'How will I know which contractor is the man for us?'

'You'll never learn younger,' said my Father with an apparent air of unconcern. 'Try asking around the local market.'

I set up shop in the empty farm cottage which was pretty cold. The winter of 1962 in fact was so cold the washing-up water froze in the bowl overnight. But I was young and fit, and keen to make my mark. How on earth could I find a contractor and what should I ask him to do? The depth of my ignorance started to dawn on me as I sat huddled in a cold sleeping bag waiting for the water to boil and heat the first of a long succession of Fray Bentos steak and kidney puddings. There was a tremendous bang on the door, which burst open to allow in a blast of freezing air and a very large, smiling young man.

'I'm your new neighbour, call me David. Anything I can do, I'm just off to market?' Just off to market!

'Hello, yes, I'm Dan, could I come too?'

'Certainly,' said my new neighbour.

We set off through the winding high-hedged roads at breakneck speed in David's old Morris van. After a few attempts to shout over the noise of the engine, which had a broken exhaust, I gave up and left him to concentrate on the road. When we arrived I confessed to David that what I needed was a reliable contractor.

'Nothing easier,' said David, 'Come and meet old George.' Old George proved to be in his mid forties but he already had his son in the business, also called George, so it was 'Old George' and 'Young George' to avoid confusion.

'George,' said David, 'this is Dan, just down from up country and he could do with a hand.'

'Yes'm,' said George.

'Pleased to meet you,' I said.

'Yes'm,' said George.

'Look,' I said importantly, 'I've got to get some spring cash crops sown and need some help. Are you the man I'm looking for?'

'Yes'm,' said George.

'Ah . . . well . . . could you come and have a look round tomorrow, then?' I asked.

'Yes'm,' said George, smiling in a friendly fashion, and with that he turned his back on me and commenced an animated conversation with his companion. I was a bit disconcerted but left it at that. David assured me on the way home that George was a reliable fellow, if a man of few words.

'You may find him a bit hard to understand, though,' he smiled to himself and bade me goodbye, leaving me to tackle the congealed remains of the Fray Bentos pie for tea.

Old George turned up the next morning in an ancient Land Rover and we set off round the farm.

'Bit o'twitch,' he remarked to nobody in particular as we walked over the first field.

'Oh,' I said. 'Twitch?'

'Yes'm,' he replied. We progressed to the next field which had been in barley the year before and been left as bare stubble. 'Plough and till I reckon,' he volunteered.

'Yes, please,' I guessed wildly. 'If that's what's needed.'

'Yes'm,' said George. 'Barley or dredge?'

Barley or dredge? I knew what barley was of course, but what had dredging got to do with it?

'Yes'm,' I replied at my wit's end. George looked at me silently for a minute.

'Us'll start on the new moon,' he said, 'but not Friday!' And with that he departed!

I consulted David who laughed a good deal. 'You're pretty new to farming then, Dan?' he asked kindly.

'Yes, I am, David,' I confessed, 'and I'm beginning to realize I can use all the help I can get!' David laughed again and explained my strange conversation. 'Twitch' was couch grass, a vigorous weed and a sign of bad farming. Tilling was the local expression for sowing, and dredge was a mixture of oats and barley.

'What about the new moon and Friday?' I asked.

'Ah,' said David, 'we're a superstitious lot down here and it's generally accepted that nothing grows too well if it's planted before the new moon. Also it's very bad luck to start a job on Friday.'

'Bad luck on Friday?' I asked. 'Does that mean you work at weekends?'

'No,' David smiled, 'we generally leave it till Monday!'

I owned up to George that I was a raw beginner and he took me under his wing, which was just as well as Father wasn't much help. I'd been ringing him up every other day to ask for advice but that had come to a sticky end so to speak.

'Hello, Dan, how are things going?' Father would ask.

'Well, we're ready to start sowing but it's a bit sticky – do you think it's too wet?'

'How should I know?' said Father.

I gave him more information. 'Well, if you walk round the field the mud sticks to your boots a bit.'

'Leave it a couple of days, then,' said Father.

'I don't think that's right,' I'd reply. 'George reckons we could make a start.'

'Well, get on with it then,' said Father, sounding a bit short.

'Yes, but what happens if the weather breaks up? George says if it goes in too firm the seed won't come through so well . . . Father, Father, are you there?' He'd ring off in disgust, but fortunately George was more patient. Father came down after about a month.

'Hm,' he said. 'Barley's gone in a bit firm, don't you think, George?'

'Yes'm,' said George. The blighter!

'Pity you didn't take my advice and leave it a couple more days, Dan.'

'Look, Father,' I started . . .

'And by the way,' Father went on, 'you'll need some stock to get on top of the grass. I'll send you down a bunch of store cattle.'

This was more like it. Store cattle from the home farm! They were bound to be a good lot of beasts and I could show David that we meant business in the new venture. The cattle turned up a few days later in two large lorries.

'Hello, Dan,' greeted the driver. His firm did all Father's local work and the trip was a real day out. 'You'll need to have good fences to hold this lot. They've been running on the downs and haven't been handled for ages. We had the dickens of a job to get them on the lorry, in fact, they kicked the side out of my regular wagon and I had to drive down in Joe's!'

Heavens! what had I been sent; was this some practical joke from Syd? I peered into the lorry and there was a wild-eyed Ayrshire steer that snorted and blew wetly at me.

'How many have you got on, Fred?' I asked the driver.

'Thirty-four,' said Fred. 'They're about two years old, a mixed bunch of steers and heifers.' When we'd backed the first lorry into position, Fred lowered the ramp and the cattle sensing something was up, started bawling loudly. *Crash . . . bang . . .*

'Heck, Dan, let's get them off before they smash this lorry as well,' Fred said, and he hurriedly opened the gate. Out came the motley snorting crew and off they went charging straight across the field and disappearing down the slope at the far end. The second lot were no better and rushed off in the same direction. After giving Fred and his mate a cup of tea and ten shillings, I went down the field to have a good look at my new charges. Not a sign! After a thorough examination I found where they'd gone through the fence across a stream and up through a small plantation and so on to the next door farm; well, some of them, for as I found next day they'd then split up. The next few days I spent claiming cattle and apologizing to every farm within three miles. So all my new neighbours had a good look at the family cattle, but perhaps Charlie, who had a pedigree beef herd, put local opinion best.

'You ought to quieten those beasts down, boy. If they come by here again I'll turn them out on the main road and good luck to you.' Humbly I apologized, and on David's advice started feeding out hay every day. Eventually they did quieten down and after a while I was pleased with their progress.

At last the time came to take them to market. This would be quite an outing: my first sale of stock. You were definitely judged on the quality of your stock in the local farming community and sorting cattle for market was an important job; but I decided to do the job on my own, and not ask advice from Father, George or David. I'd looked after the cattle for nearly nine months and I reckoned I was getting a useful eye for stock. I picked out a nice bunch of ten heifers, arranged with the haulier and booked them into market for the following Friday. Now the locals would see what I was made of.

'Shall I sell them in pairs or put them in as a bunch, sir?' asked the auctioneer as we stood together on his rostrum over-looking the sale ring.

'What's the best way?' I asked.

'Well, if they're in goodish order I'd sell them in pairs. Some of the smaller farmers like to buy a couple of good beasts to run after the dairy cows.'

'Right,' I said. 'Pairs it is, and let's see if you can get a good price. You won't have better animals to sell today!' In came the first two heifers, coats shining with health. This was the big moment.

''Ere,' a voice from the ring called out, 'that one's in calf!' In calf, what on earth did the fellow mean?

'Is one in calf, sir?' the auctioneer asked me.

'Certainly not,' I said, 'they've been nowhere near a bull.'

'She's in calf,' said the voice.

'Definitely springing,' another added.

'Yes, in calf,' added several more.

Red-faced, I looked at the auctioneer. 'Well, she's not in calf, but as those fellows are adamant what can be done?'

'I think you'd better take her home, sir, that would be the best bet,' he replied. So the heifer was separated and run back to the loading pens. The other nine sold well enough despite a loud question from the ringside that was greeted with a few sniggers. 'Any more in calf, boy?' I left the market with what little dignity I had left and took the heifer in question home. The very next day she gave birth to a fine bull calf.

'Well, Dan,' said David, who'd come to oversee the birth. 'You've still got a bit to learn. She must have taken Charlie's bull when the whole bunch were doing their tour of the countryside. You ought to let me pick the next bunch you want to send to market.'

I took David's advice and vowed that when the cattle were disposed of I'd replace them with a flock of sheep. At least there, my experience at home and in Australia would come in handy and I could show the locals a thing or two.

NETTON

It's funny how you learn about things. The last place I expected to hear about Netton Farm was in the middle of a windswept Wiltshire down. I'd come up to Tangley, from Devon, to try and persuade Father to sell me some vital bit of machinery or other that I needed. Whilst I was at Tangley I'd offered to check the sheep on the downland farm about six miles from my parents' house. The downland farm was very isolated and I'd been surprised to spot a lone figure walking across the open fields. When I caught up with the figure, it turned out to be a nice enough chap who was out bird-watching.

'Marvellous place, this. You see nearly as many species here as we used to get on the family estate in Devon.'

'Where's that?' I asked, out of polite interest.

'Ah, a place called Revelstoke near Noss Mayo in South Devon. You wouldn't know of it. It's no longer in the family, of course.'

'Well!' I said, 'I've just started farming there! Netton Farm, it's called.'

'Netton Farm! Good Lord!' and the bird-watcher told me all about the Revelstoke family and their estate.

*

It wasn't a very big estate and, as I remember, the Revelstoke family didn't have it very long. Whilst they did, however, they spent a great deal of money making it ship-shape. Netton Farm House was built in 1881. It wasn't the original house on the farm and it was very posh for a tenant's farmhouse – built of local stone and slate from the estate's quarries. Apparently, when it was finished, the owner came round to see if all was OK, to find that the farmer was only using three of the four big reception rooms – the fourth was in use as a coal and wood store. As a result the next farmhouse for a tenant to be built on the estate was exactly the same design as Netton, but with one room less downstairs and upstairs. They sort of took a bite out of it, no doubt at vast architectural expense, but the landlord insisted, pointing out that farmers didn't need four reception rooms, did they!

This rather grand attitude extended to the land. The Revelstokes built a nine-mile carriageway as a sort of afternoon drive around the estate, about two miles of which was along the cliffs at Netton. The carriageway was hewn out of solid rock – actually, the rock's not all that solid, it's a 'soft' slate locally called 'shillet' – but it was still a major operation, and all done by hand. According to the bird-watcher I met, the road gang took a year or so to complete the project, and reported a job well done in mid winter when other work was a bit slack. Lady Revelstoke, on hearing the men would be out of work, ordered the drive to be made three feet wider! Unfortunately the opulence didn't last. The family came on hard times before the First World War, and thanks to a dodgy investment in Argentine railways, the estate was sold.

Netton was purchased, along with two sister farms, by the local Co-op and turned into a thriving dairy farm, producing milk for the Co-op's retail outlets. The Co-op eventually decided to quit large-scale farming and concentrate on selling. At the time my father bought Netton they were milking 80-odd cows which employed eleven men.

The cows were tied up in stalls in a long barn with all their food brought by hand and wheelbarrows. The milking was done by buckets plugged into an airline, then ran the length of the shed – each cow being milked individually. Then the buckets were tipped into churns that were wheeled singly to the dairy. It was very labour-intensive and not the sort of farming that father and I agreed I might be capable of! This meant nine of the eleven men had to go – very sad indeed – and I had the job of sorting out who I should offer work to.

I was planning to grow corn and keep sheep. I knew something about sheep, but very little else, so what I needed pretty desperately was someone who could turn his hand to anything. I asked Basil, the manager. Basil was off to run a small farm of his own in Cornwall.

'You won't do better than Preston,' Basil said. 'He's been on the farm over twenty years and he can do whatever job you want – thatch a rick, build a stone wall, lay a hedge . . . anything.' Lay a hedge . . . build a wall? What on earth had that to do with modern farming? I planned to knock most of the hedges down anyway!

'Er . . . you say Preston's been here twenty years. How old is he?' I asked cautiously.

'Oh, not much more than forty,' said Basil, who was getting on that way himself; at least compared to me at twenty-five he was!

'Forty! That's a bit old! Is he still fit enough?'

Basil laughed, catching my drift. 'Don't you worry, Dan,' he said kindly, 'Preston'll work you off your feet and then go on for hours! You really won't do any better, I can assure you of that.'

So Preston was to be number one tractor man. But I still needed someone fit and willing to try his hand at sheep. He had to be game to put up with some of the ideas I'd picked up in New Zealand and Australia as well.

'Try John,' said Basil, 'he's honest as the day is long and will have a go at anything if you tell him what to do.'

So that was that, and thanks to Basil I had a team to help me through the next twenty years or so.

You'll meet John properly later on. He became my right-hand man with the sheep, but Preston was the one who looked after the arable side, so whilst John and I were busy lambing or shearing, Preston had to get on with things more or less on his own. I relied on him totally. Basil was absolutely right about Preston's ability to work. Whatever the job, he simply kept going until it was done. I'd try and keep up with him swinging an axe or thumping in fence posts, but it was no good. Talk about the hare and the tortoise. After a couple of hours I'd have to find an excuse – a telephone call or an urgent trip to market – before slinking off to my office to recover! I'd come back an hour later and Preston would still be at it, at exactly the same pace.

He hadn't done much tractor work for the Co-op – quite simply he'd been in too much demand fixing and mending things. But I needn't have worried, he took to ploughing, drilling and combining with the same meticulous precision and good humour as he used when building a dry stone wall, and the result was the same. With Preston in charge the work was always on time and excellently done.

For more than twenty years he'd have his lunch sitting in the cart linney – an old open-fronted stone and slate building halfway up a steep track leading out of the main farmyard. When he'd eaten his sandwiches and cake he'd sit on an old car seat, legs crossed in front of him, totally at peace with the world and relaxed, cloth cap pulled down over his eyes. More often than not the robin that was resident in the cart linney would be sitting bright-eyed and intelligent, having had his share of Preston's lunch. One of the robin's favourite perches was Preston's boot. So there you have it. Preston was a true country-man and a real paragon of virtue. In all our time together he only let me down once.

After ten years or so at Netton I was offered the chance to do some work in television. A producer in Plymouth, who should have known better, was making six or seven items – a sort of

Cherrington's eye view of farming. I thought it would be a good idea to interview Preston. He'd be able to tell the viewers what a grand life it was being a farm worker; back to nature and all that, I told the producer. Long-sufferingly Mike agreed to my enthusiastic idea and, muttering something about 'paternalism', he got us lined up in front of the camera. I told Preston not to worry, just to forget we were there and to relax. I hope he didn't notice how my knees were knocking. Then Mike said, 'Action.'

'Now, Preston,' I said, 'you've been working here on Netton Farm for more than thirty years. If you had your life all over again would you do just the same and be a farm worker?'

'No,' answered Preston. No?! That hadn't been in the script, surely? I pressed blindly on.

'Why not?' I asked.

'You don't pay me enough,' said Preston.

'CUT . . . CUT . . .' said Mike, grinning delightedly. 'Splendid stuff. We'll use it just as it is!'

When I first started at Netton neither Preston nor John had travelled much. (Mind you, John's really caught the bug now and he's just as likely to take a trip to Yugoslavia for his holiday as he is to go to Brighton or Bognor.) They were both very interested to meet my father. He appeared regularly on television at that time and wrote in farming journals, so the fact that John Cherrington was the boss's father was a real bonus. Father got on well with anybody in farming and he suggested that Preston and John might enjoy a day out on the family farm in Hampshire.

'Go to Tangley? That would be a proper job . . . Yes, proper, Dan. We'd really like that.' They were both as keen as mustard. For some reason I was to be away in Hampshire for a few days so I suggested they could catch a train from Plymouth and I'd pick them up from Andover Junction about five miles from Tangley Farm in Hampshire.

'You could take the farm van to Plymouth Station,' I suggested, 'I'll drive us back in my car.'

'Plymouth Station?' said John blankly.

'Yes, the railway station,' I said. 'You know where it is, surely?'

'Ah, yes,' said John doubtfully.

'You'll need to change at Exeter,' I said, 'but you'll only have half an hour to wait for the Andover train. I'll meet you at Andover. You're due in at ten thirty; that'll give us all day to look round.' I trailed off.

'Right,' said John after a bit.

'Is that OK, Preston?' I asked.

'Oh, yes,' said Preston, a bit vaguely.

'Shall I write the times down?' I asked.

'You'd better,' said John.

After this rather confusing conversation we got busy on farm work and I forgot all about the trip – I couldn't imagine anything would go wrong. I'd given John the telephone number at Tangley in case the train was delayed.

The following week I duly met the train from Exeter at Andover station. Ten thirty: it was dead on time . . . but no Preston and no John. What on earth could have happened? I went to the enquiry office and checked the Plymouth/Exeter train times. No, there had been no delays: half an hour at Exeter to change trains – plenty of time. Disappointed, I supposed the farm van must have broken down. All I could do was to go back to Tangley and wait until they telephoned. Meanwhile the next train was due just after twelve.

I went back to Tangley. No word from John and Preston. Oh well, I thought, they must be on the twelve o'clock. So in I went to meet it. No John, no Preston. Back to Tangley, and shortly before one o'clock the phone rang.

'Hello, Dan, is that you?' It was John. 'We're still here,' he said. 'There's a train to Andover that gets in at three thirty. Shall we catch that?'

'Where's here?' I asked.

'What?' said John, putting another shilling in the phone.

'Where are you?' I asked.

'We're at Exeter,' John said. 'We've been here since eight o'clock!' I agreed that I'd pick them up at three thirty, and they duly arrived, rather to my surprise, just in time for tea at Tangley before we had to set out back to Devon in my car.

'What went wrong at Exeter?' I asked, as we drove out to Tangley.

Preston laughed. 'We didn't realize the Andover train went from a different platform,' he said. 'We just waited on platform three where the Plymouth train came in. It wasn't until gone ten that we realized something was wrong – then we asked a porter; but by then we'd missed the next train as well!'

'How on earth . . .?' I started.

'Well,' said Preston, 'it was like this. I've never been on a train, you see, and John's only been on one once.'

When you think about, it's perfectly logical if there's one track coming into the station and one track going out, then all the trains ought to stop at the same platform, and, as John pointed out, I'd said to get out at Exeter and wait there for the Andover train.

'Well, you're here now,' I said, 'and although we won't get much of a look at Tangley we can stop at a pub on the way home and have a jolly good feed and a pint of beer.'

'Ah,' said Preston, 'I've never been in a pub. Never seen the point really.'

As I've said, Netton was a dairy farm when my father bought it, but we were looking for a farm that could grow corn and would suit sheep. Netton was ideal. It's right on the coast, four or five miles east of Plymouth as the crow flies – well, perhaps as a gull might fly, as you have to cross the sea if you follow a straight line. There were 130 acres or so of steep cliff land which my father and I discounted. 'If you couldn't plough it, then it wasn't much use:' that was his dictum and I accepted it as gospel; at least when we first went round the farm I did. What attracted us were the 380 acres or so of free-draining, easy working soil that was more or less level along the cliff tops.

'There are too many fields, Father,' I said. 'One of the first jobs will be to take out some of these banks and walls.'

Thanks to the Dig-for-Victory mentality that still infected the Ministry of Agriculture in those days you actually got paid to rip out hedges, banks and other forms of wildlife sanctuary that littered the countryside.

'I shouldn't be in too much of a hurry, Dan,' my father said. 'Some of those banks were put here for a very good reason, and you need shelter for the sheep.' He pointed at a stunted thorn tree growing horizontally out of the top of a Devon bank. 'You can see from that old thorn that the weather can be really rough.'

I'd expected this conservatism. 'Ah, but that's not the power of the wind, but the salt in the air. The thorn doesn't like salt, so it favours the inland side for growing.'

'Hm,' said Father. 'I think gales in the spring and autumn could be pretty fierce. Look, instead of taking all the hedges out at once, why don't you start with the half dozen or so that are really obvious? You can always have another go later, and you can't put them back.'

I allowed myself to be persuaded, although I was desperately keen to get everything done at once. Still, might as well humour Father . . . he was backing the venture, after all. The half dozen walls and banks were duly taken out by Young George on an old International bulldozer. Father had come to Netton to see how things were progressing.

'Make it a bit fresh up here when it blows!' George observed as we surveyed the fine new twenty-acre field he'd created from two smaller ones.

'Ah, yes, but see how much easier it'll be to work,' I said.

'Not so much shelter, though,' George replied. The blighter, I thought. He hadn't minded taking on the work!

'Just what I told Dan,' said Father.

'Well,' I answered, stung by this double attack, 'sheep have legs . . . they can walk over to that wall just as easily!'

George laughed. 'There's a few stones left to pick up,' he

said. 'Us didn't like to dig out any more of the old wall, 'twould have taken all the soil. Pity you didn't dray the foyer before we started,' he finished.

'Dray the foyer? . . . What on earth's that?' asked my father.

'Well,' said George, 'I doesn't suppose you do that in Hampshire with all that land, but down here, particularly if the fields are a bit slopy, the soil tends to get worked down to the bottom of the field over the years. The job used to be to plough a few "foyers" – that's furrows – with the plough, then to dray the earth back to the top of the field in a horse and cart to cover up the bony bits . . . you know, where the rock's showing through!'

'Well,' I said, 'I can't afford the time and I haven't got a horse and cart! I'll hitch up the big ripper to the tractor to work out the hedge line. We can pick up the stones by hand.'

'You'll have a brave few loads, then,' said George dolefully. 'Real stony this bank was. Don't think I'd have taken her out myself . . .' Father nodded in agreement.

Well, I thought, I'll show them. I'll get the ground ripped out and the stones picked up in no time!

It took days and days.

'Pity Basil sent me out here last winter,' said Preston good humouredly, as he and I picked yet another trailer load. 'I must have spent nearly a month making up gaps . . . hauled tons of stone out here to do it! It'll be a bit bleak here, come October!'

Such is the reluctance to change, I thought . . . It so happened that I decided to give the ground where the old wall and bank had been one more good ripping over before the whole field was ploughed that autumn. It was my first experience of a gale. The tractors, in those days, didn't have cabs, and the force of the wind literally took my breath away as I drove slowly up and down the field. The sky was black as the ace of spades, and I must have been right in the middle of the field when it started to rain. At least, it must have started as rain when it left the scudding clouds rushing over head; when it hit me it felt more like machine-gun bullets. I was soaked to the skin in less than five minutes, despite a heavy overcoat, and as the sheets of rain swept across the big, bare field, it was impossible to look into the storm and breathe. You simply sucked in water.

Hell, I thought, this is no fun, and I turned and drove the tractor away from the cliffs and kept going until I came to the field boundary – a six-foot-high solid stone wall – top of the list for George's bulldozer in the spring! I left the tractor and climbed awkwardly onto the top of the wall in my wet heavy clothes, and was literally blown off, to land in a heap on the lee side . . . the difference was extraordinary! I sat with my back to the wall in an oasis of peace, the solid stone shrugging off the full fury of a south-west gale without a tremor as I waited for a break in the rain. I decided enough was enough. I couldn't re-build the banks we'd taken out already, but perhaps there was some merit in leaving the remaining ones that were still standing.

It's difficult to explain just how powerful a force-ten gale can be, but at Netton there's nothing between you and the Atlantic. If it really blows, then on the exposed parts of the farm it's literally impossible to stand.

Even when the rain abated on the day I experienced my first gale there was real proof of how hard the wind had been blowing when I got back to the tractor. Despite the fact that it had been raining cats and dogs for half hour or so, the seat was totally dry – the force of the wind had blown the raindrops across the open field so hard that it had truly rained horizontally.

SHEEP

It's funny, looking back, but the only practical training in farming I received was how to look after sheep. The reason was that
Father had a cowman for the cows, a pigman for the pigs, and
each tractor driver had his particular block of land to plough.
Father was particularly keen on sheep, however, and with four
sons growing up more or less in succession, he relied on us to do
the leg work and dispensed with a regular shepherd. This was
all well and good, and I had learnt how to lamb a ewe and pick
fat lambs for the market at a pretty tender age, *but* it didn't
mean I had been trained in the art of sheep management . . .

'Nice lot of sheep, Dan,' my neighbour, David, said as we leant
over the gate looking at my new flock.

'Thanks,' I said proudly. With Syd's help I'd bought four
hundred 'mule' ewes from the north of England as the basis of
my sheep enterprise. These fit, active sheep are bred in the
Lake District – no big, fat, dozy South Devon sheep for me!

'Jumpers, are they?' David asked, as one hopped on to a dead
tree stump a good three feet off the ground without really exert-
ing herself.

'No,' I said, 'not especially.'

'You may have to fence them a bit, though,' said David. 'These old banks are fine for South Devon ewes – we say a shadow across the gateway'll keep them in. But these . . . 'mules' . . . is that what you call them? They look a bit more active!'

Fencing: I hadn't really thought of that. It might mean having to fence each side of the Devon banks that divided the fields. Heavens! If that was the case it might have been cheaper to buy Devon long wools.

'All maidens, are they?' David's next question broke into my thoughts.

'Yes, absolutely,' I replied. Maidens meant they were all young sheep, eighteen months old, in fact, that hadn't lambed before. To be specific it meant they haven't met any rams yet, so I suppose 'maiden' is a pretty apt description. David looked sceptical.

'I wanted to make sure I kept disease out of the flock, particularly abortion. (Abortion is a real bane for sheep farmers, and generally maidens were infected by being put into a flock with older sheep.)

'Ah,' said David, 'I was just thinking that maidens can be a bit skittish. You know, sometimes they're not so good at being mothers, taking to their lambs – but maybe these . . . "mules", is that what you call them? . . . are better than local sheep!'

Got it, I thought, he's just a bit jealous that I was the one to bring mules to the area! Ah well, innovators are never understood.

He was right about the fencing, of course, although the sheep behaved very well at first – whilst I had plenty of grass. Then they had a great time getting to know the rams. After that they lived the life of Riley eating stubble turnips and kale until February. In February I tried to get them interested in hay, and bought concentrate feed which I fed to them in troughs. They didn't think much of that, and without any older sheep to help them settle down to a proper winter feed regime, decided that the grass looked much greener next door.

I spent a couple of weeks trying to patch holes in the hedges, until one night they walked up the road and demolished four acres of rye corn that David had grown as early bite for his cows.

'Look, neighbour,' he said grimly, 'I suggest you get your sheep fenced properly, otherwise . . .'

I decided he was right, and started off by fencing in the lambing field. I'd learned a bit about lambing in New Zealand and had decided I'd lamb outside. The idea was to divide the lambing area into 6 or 8 paddocks and move the ewes through to a new paddock each day. Once the lambs were 4 or 5 days old they could be shifted to other fields not in the system. A great theory, but it ignored one vital ingredient. March in Devon can be very, very wet.

That year – 1964 it was – it started raining in February and just kept going, day after day. It simply didn't let up. The ground became saturated, and because my lambing field had been freshly sown the previous autumn, it didn't soak up the water like an old pasture, but became a sea of mud – well, not quite mud – the grass kept growing, so it was more like a rice paddy with green shoots poking out of the wet sloppy surface.

The result was that the lambs were born wet, onto wet mud, in continuous rain. And I spent day after miserable day, trying to catch ewes and lambs and bring them into a dry pen at the farm for a few hours, so that they could get some sort of a start in life.

The crunch came at three o'clock one morning, after about a fortnight. The ewes were in a sloping paddock just above the cliffs, and I was driving carefully around with my two dogs breathing down my neck, looking for trouble. David had also been right about the maidens, of course. The young ewes were atrocious mothers. As often as not, they'd have their lambs and then wander off bleating madly, wondering what on earth had been going on without bothering to look round to see the result of their labours.

'There's one, Scotty,' I said to my big male sheepdog. 'Look at her, she's had one and is about to have another – right in the muddiest part of the field!'

Scott panted eagerly in my left ear as he peered through the windscreen trying to see what was going on through the driving, sleety rain . . . The ewe had lambed in a small hollow, and her bedraggled offspring was struggling to get up, half submerged in the muddy water. His mother, meanwhile, was lying on her side a few yards away straining to give birth to a second lamb. I groaned inwardly, thinking of the wam bed I'd left ten minutes ago, and Sandy's sleepy . . . 'Are you all right?' . . . as I'd slipped into my last pair of dry trousers. Scott panted, and then with a final heave the ewe produced another offspring into the ice cold wet mud. It struggled convulsively, and its mother got up and started to wander off downhill.

'Blast the bloody creature! It's not even going to clean off the lamb! Here Scott! Here Flash!' I jumped out of the van and we headed towards the ewe.

'Come bye, dogs!' I sent the dogs away to head her off, the idea being that the mother would remember her maternal instincts and come trotting back to protect her offspring. Some hope! She took one look at Scott and took off.

'Hold her! Hold her!' I shouted, knowing that if we lost her in the dark any chance of her wanting the lambs by the time we'd sorted her out in the morning would be gone, and I'd have a couple more orphans to look after. Scott did his stuff, and immediately leapt for the ewe, catching her by the fleece on the shoulder, then digging in his feet and putting all his weight into trying to slow the ewe down. I ran headlong down the slope towards them, but the slope got steeper and the ewe picked up speed as she went downhill. Flash, my little bitch, dashed in to try and help, but was bowled head-over-heels by the now crazed ewe.

'Hold her. Hold her!' I shouted as I ran, trying to keep the torch on Scotty and the ewe. At last Scotty had some effect, and I got close enough to try and help. I leapt, and grabbed, and

slither . . . slush . . . *crash* . . . Sheep, dogs and I slid the last
ten yards to wind up enmeshed in my new fence just above the
steepest part of the cliff.

'Damn and blast you!' I swore at the unfortunate sheep. I'd
collided with a fence post that had knocked the breath out of
me. The torch had gone flying, and I'd lost my glasses; not that
I could see anything in the pitch dark. There was nothing for it,
I'd have to drag her to the van a hundred yards back up the
field. It was too wet and slippy to tie her up and bring the van
to her, even if I'd remembered to bring any rope.

It took twenty minutes to cover half the distance, what with
the mud, rain and struggling ewe. Then I slipped and fell, and
the ewe escaped my icy clutch.

'Hold her, Scott, hold her.' And in thirty seconds or so we
were back at the fence.

I remember actually crying with sheer frustration. When
eventually I'd got the ewe into the van, both lambs had drowned
in the puddle they'd been born into. On the way back to the
farm I decided we'd have to give up trying to lamb the ewes
outside and bring them into the corn barn. If we all worked like
beavers, we ought to be able to make enough pens for the ewes
as they lambed, and anything would be better than this.

First thing next morning David turned up – I don't know
what sixth sense tells neighbours when they're wanted, but all
he said was, 'I thought you might need a hand. Are you going
to bring them in?'

By eight that night everything was under cover. Every building had ewes and lambs in; every corner its little family; and the
largest barn was home for 80 ewes and 150 or so lambs. None of
them was more than four days old and the whole lot were in an
indescribable muddle, trying to sort themselves out into who-
belonged-to-who.

'We'll leave them to it,' I said (in truth I was completely
knackered) 'and see how many have sorted themselves out by
morning . . . at least they're dry!'

I went to bed listening to the steady rain – happy for the first time in two weeks that it wouldn't kill any more lambs that night. Next morning we had the first two cases of contagious pneumonia. The lambs had come in wet, and warmed up too quickly in the steamy heat of the barn. On top of this we had at least 30 lambs nobody wanted. The ewes had settled down all right – a fair percentage had settled for no-responsibility-thank-you.

By the time the sun shone and the sheep went out, the pneumonia had killed more than 20 lambs, and we had to rear 15 orphans, even after the determined efforts to 'mother up' spare lambs to ewes that refused to admit they'd ever been robbed of their virginity! I swore I'd never lamb outside again. Indoor lambing was all the rage, and by next year we'd be properly organized.

After that disastrous start, most of the lambings were a piece of cake. To make enough room under cover I used to hire a big marquee from the tent manufacturers in town. As long as we finished in time for Easter weddings they were happy to give me a very keen price, and it worked a treat. You did have to hang onto the guy ropes if the weather really blew up, but we only lost one tent in ten years. The other thing you had to put up with was a few comments at the odd reception held on a hot day. 'This tent's a bit niffy – did you clean it properly after the sheep? No dead ones left in the corners?'

The only other disaster was when the dreaded abortion struck. It was the worst experience of my farming life, and I don't think I've really worried about anything since.

I'd been farming several years by then, and was running 2,000 ewes split into several flocks. The abortion hit one flock of 600 ewes about six weeks before lambing.

'They just won't eat this morning, Boss,' John reported. He'd been feeding concentrates and hay that day.

'Won't eat, John? What on earth do you mean? They normally knock you over to get at the concentrates.'

'I know, Boss, but not this morning. At least half of them just stood around looking sleepy.'

'I'll take a look,' I said, and went straight off to check the flock in the farm van. John was right. There was the hay, fresh in the racks, hardly touched. The concentrates were still in the feed troughs with barely a handful of ewes poking their noses at it disconsolately. With sinking heart I walked through the flock. The ewes that had been bright and friendly the last time I'd seen them two days before were dull and listless. Then I spotted one with telltale blood around her behind. Abortion! I looked more carefully and spotted two more. Then, as I walked, I came upon the first foetus, perfectly formed but at least six weeks premature . . .

I went straight home and rang the vet who came that afternoon.

'I'll take some tests, Mr Cherrington. But I've no doubt this is contagious abortion. You must expect quite a few more, I'm afraid. These infections come in storms – it could go on several weeks. All you can do is try and pick out the ewes that abort and treat them with antibiotic to stop any secondary infection.'

We caught three ewes that had obviously lost their lambs and the vet took samples of blood in bottles for testing. He went after an hour or so and left supplies of antibiotic.

The third morning was the worst, when I picked up 80 foetuses. The ewes kept aborting right up to lambing. Even when we started getting live lambs a fair percentage were sickly and weak, whilst their mothers had barely enough milk to keep them going. All in all, 150 ewes aborted out of the 600, and we buried more than 300 lambs. If it hadn't been for the skill and enthusiasm of the lambing team it would have been many more.

It's amazing how one comes to terms with the black depression that tragedies of this sort engender, but either you do, or you give up keeping livestock – and it's easy to forget the good times.

One good time, or at least good idea, I first saw in New Zealand. I was on a learning trip after I'd been farming on my own account for fifteen years or so.

'Plastic macs,' said Kerry, my New Zealand host. 'Plastic macs for lambs – that's what they are!'

We were in Kerry's large airy sheep shed and wool store, and he had been showing me some of the new ideas on the market in New Zealand. 'The idea is that when it looks like the weather is going to be really rough we dash round and fit any very young or weak lambs with "macs". They're specially shaped with head and leg holes. You can even get little ones for triplets!'

Remembering that disastrous first lambing, I was fascinated, and quite determined to try the macs out on my own flock. As it happened, the next spring was warm and dry for just about the whole of lambing, and the little plastic coats I'd made lay idle in the sheep store. Then, right at the tail end, we had a really nasty couple of days. Most of the lambs were big and strong, but we had one very small lot of triplets.

'Are you going to leave them out?' Sandy asked in surprise. 'It's bound to rain again tonight, and it's really cold.'

I looked at the old ewe and her three little offspring. She was as proud as punch and there was absolutely no way she would desert them.

'Yes, I'm going to try the lamb macs,' I said, 'there'll never be a better test. She's a great mother, and although they're small they're bright enough. I'll put them in the paddock by the house so I can check them first thing in the morning.'

We put one of the specially small macs I'd made for little lambs on each of the triplets. They were still plenty big enough, and the lambs looked like children wearing Dad's overcoat. The ewe made a bit of a fuss, nuzzling each lamb carefully, to check it was hers under its strange new coat, but she soon made up her mind they were indeed her offspring and led them protectively away across the paddock to seek the shelter of the hedge. The little lambs followed, bright blue macs touching the ground lightly. It looked as though the macs themselves were moving. Each one with its own driver whose little bright-eyed head stuck out of the top to see where they were going.

The dawn was grey with rain lashing down, and the paddock

beside the house was sodden and inhospitable as I looked out of the window. Where was the old ewe; what about the triplets? In the murky light I spotted the old ewe grazing in the middle of the paddock in the full force of the driving rain. Then my heart stopped . . . one . . . two . . . three . . . There was no mistake. Three crumpled plastic heaps lay on the ground a few yards from the mother. Why had I been so stupid? I might as well have shot the poor little beggars. But why had the sheep taken her lambs out into the open; why hadn't she stayed in the shelter of the hedge?

I opened the window and yelled at the stupid sheep in anger and frustration. 'You stupid old bag. Why . . .'

At the sound of my voice . . . pop . . . pop . . . pop . . . Three little heads popped out of three snug, warm, plastic mobile homes, and hop . . . skip . . . jump . . . the triplets, fit as fiddles, went joyfully for a quick breakfast from Mum, completely oblivious of the inclement weather.

COMBINES

Getting started in farming is pretty tough on the pocket – for at least six months it's spend, spend, spend; even with the crop in the barn you then have to wait for the best price before you sell. So it can be up to twelve months before you get any money back. I was trained as an agricultural economist but when it came to getting my own farm under way it wasn't so much a question of cash flows, more a matter of a bottomless pit. To help out and speed up harvest Father offered to send a second combine down from the home farm; this would mean I could put off buying a larger machine for another year, and as Devon was a good deal earlier than the Hampshire hills, we reckoned I could get well over half my acreage done before he was ready to start.

'What about a driver?' I enquired. 'Preston is OK but I need to keep an eye on the dryer.' This was a bit of a snide remark as the grain dryer was an original Alvin Blanch model built at the end of the war. It had been too slow for Father and Syd so they'd got a new updated version whilst I, like the perennial younger brother, had been presented with the cast-off. I'd designed a drying and storage system around the old dryer in a converted cow shed that Emmett would have been proud of – full of theory and secondhand parts including a grain cleaner that was originally driven by steam. Nobody was too keen to test whether the system would work and even I admitted it might have a few teething problems. This meant I couldn't take on driving the combine; I'd need another member for the team.

'Very well,' said Father, 'I'll send George down.' I was impressed: George was a bachelor, so quite happy to have a couple of weeks in the West Country and as he was a fully qualified combine driver he'd be just the ticket.

'Great,' I said to Father, 'could you send him down the first week in August?'

'How on earth will we get it off?' John, the all-purpose member of my team, asked. Preston just shook his head.

'We loaded it off a proper ramp in Hampshire,' said George helpfully. George was a seriously humorous Hampshire man with forearms the size of tree trunks. He'd follow a leader anywhere but wasn't too keen to be in front of the boss, however young and inexperienced. The lorry driver and I looked glumly at the massive red combine squatting on the back of the adapted cattle waggon like some sort of demented vulture – its large driving wheels on the very edge on each side of the bed of the lorry.

'It did sway a bit on the way down,' announced the driver with mournful relish. 'And the whole lot really lurched when Syd drove it on.' The combine glowered at us with its driving seat a good fifteen feet off the ground. 'You'll drive it off, then?' enquired George. 'It's not my regular machine.'

Hell, I thought, I am the boss, and Syd drove the damn thing on; but where on earth could we get it off without any proper ramp? Preston, ever resourceful, suggested that if we backed the lorry against the roadside bank of the small field in front of the house; and if we took the fence down, we could jack the bed of the lorry up to stop it swaying on its springs; use a few sleepers . . .

'Just hold her on the clutch . . .' George was directing operations from the road . . . 'you may find the brakes aren't too good . . .' It wasn't so much a matter of not too good; there were no brakes at all. I thought about stopping operations to see if we could bleed some life into the brakes but then I thought better of it, it had taken all my bravado to get up into the driving seat. I hung on grimly and, revving up the engine, inched forward in the lowest gear. George shouted and mimed helpfully.

'Left a bit . . . try right hand down . . . mind the sleeper . . .' I couldn't see anything of what was going on underneath so I decided to press on . . . 'Don't turn the back wheels too sharp . . . Careful . . . WATCH IT . . . LOOK OUT SHE'S COMING OFF THE JACK!'

I felt the combine lurch, determined to turn turtle and block the road for days with me underneath. In blind panic I gave her full throttle and we lurched forward, the driving wheels slipped and juddered on the sleepers, then, just as all was lost and the ungainly machine started to slew sideways, the wheels gripped and held and the combine shot off the lorry over the hedge into the field.

'Well done, Dan,' said George.' I thought you were a goner then! Here, better let me take over, you look a bit shaky!'

George may have thought that was the end of the excitement but he hadn't had a chance of a look round the farm at that stage. One thing about Devon is that it's full of 'proper' farmers – none of your half-hearted Hampshire approach to what you can do with a bit of steep awkward land. I'd been used to leaving the odd bits of fields to the rabbits, or for a bit of pheasant cover; none of this in Devon, however. If you didn't have a suicidal determination to cultivate every available acre you weren't worth a light. Netton was right on the coast and so the fields were cropped right to the edge of the cliffs.

By two o'clock we were ready to make a start.

'Where do you reckon it'll be most forward, Preston?' I asked.

'Next to the coastguard station, I think, Dan,' Preston was

35

seldom wrong about which field would be the ripest, so we set off across the farm.

'Right, George, off you go. George?' . . . I looked around. The combines were ready for off at the edge of the ripe golden barley. The slope was concave at this point between us and the sea and all you could see looking south was the corn suddenly ending in a sparkling blue ocean three hundred feet below.

'There's George, Dan,' John laughingly shouted from his seat on the tractor. 'He's worried you're sending him for a quick dip.'

I looked across the barley and there was George very cautiously inching forward with craning neck trying to discover how far he could go without crashing onto the rocks below. Preston, John and I sat watching until George got far enough to see that the field finished in a flat headland well away from the cliff edge. He turned to trudge back up the hill, crestfallen under our grinning gaze.

'Bit steeper than you're used to then?' asked John. 'Would you like Preston to go first?' I never have got used to steep land, however, and when the combine was in a particularly bad field I always had my heart in my mouth that there'd be an accident. In the end it wasn't George that got into trouble but Preston.

'The combine's tipped over. It's going to roll right down onto the caravans!' John was almost incoherent with excitement.

'Calm down, John,' I said. 'What about Preston?'

'He's all right, a bit shaken up, though.' John had come to the farm to find me where I'd been wrestling with the dryer. He filled me in on the details as we drove back to the scene of the accident.

'Something went wrong with the brakes. She just spun round and crashed over. Right above the caravan site. She's propped up by the spout. If that goes it'll be goodbye caravans!' The field Preston had been cutting was indeed about two hundred feet directly above a large caravan site full of Midlanders who'd come down to Devon for a bit of peace and quiet. Sure enough there was the combine lodged at an impossible angle on the steepest slope; poised to roll down among the unsuspecting holidaymakers below. It had turned over directly onto its unloading spout, and was balanced precariously ready to spring into action. I walked down the slope to where Preston sat.

'Are you OK, Preston?' I asked.

'Yes, Dan,' Preston replied. 'But I feel a bit shaky. It just went. I was pulling out to turn and the brake seized on or something. It gave me a real fright. I'm sorry it happened, Dan.'

'Don't worry about it, Preston; I'm just grateful you didn't end up down in the campsite underneath the blessed thing.' *Creakkkk*. The 'blessed thing' groaned and settled more comfortably on its spout . .

'Heck, we'll have to get her up,' I said cursing myself for not having cut the steep bit myself. 'Look, you take it easy while I get some help organized.'

I sent John off to warn the caravan site of the threat hanging over them whilst I rounded up the neighbours to come and give a hand. One thing about farming is that neighbours are always ready to come and help out in a crisis especially a nice juicy one like this. Within an hour I had half a dozen tractors with strong ropes attached to the stricken machine.

'You get on top and make sure we all pull at once, Dan,' said my neighbour David.

'OK,' I said, trying to be enthusiastic. The combine had creaked and groaned whilst we had attached the ropes and I wasn't at all sure how long its unloading spout was going to hold.

'Now look, you chaps, when I raise my hand get ready, then when I lower it, all pull together. But for heaven's sake don't pull early, she could spin round and if she comes off the spout . . .'

'I reckon my tractor could do the job on its own, better than trying to get this lot pulling at the same time.' Another neighbour had sent his brand new four-wheel drive 100-horse-power machine of which the driver was justly proud. 'And as for that fart box, it's no better than a Dinky toy . .'

'It'll outlast your blessed monster,' said Jim, the owner of the 'Dinky toy' – a little grey Ferguson twenty years old and much loved by Jim who had a smallholding a couple of miles up the road. He'd heard I was in trouble by that remarkable bush tele-graph that works so well in the countryside and had turned up to offer assistance.

'Every little helps, Fred,' said David. 'Jim might just give us that extra ounce that matters.'

'Ounce is about all it's good for,' muttered Fred as he stomped off importantly to climb into the cab of his gleaming monster.

I climbed very gingerly onto the upside of the combine, ready to abandon ship in case the worst happened. Engines revved and roared as the tractors got ready. *C . . r . . . e . . a . . k . .* went the combine as they took up the slack. 'To hell with this,' I thought, and raised my hand, ready to give the signal. Jim, impatient to show Fred a thing or two, let in his clutch, and the combine came up onto its wheels without a tremor, pulled up by the little grey Fergie!

Fred didn't say a word. He got out of his tractor, unhitched his tow rope and drove away across the stubble as black as a thundercloud with Jim's words of victory ringing in his ears.

'I always knew the old girl could pull, but that combine must weigh seven tons. Well, I'm blowed, what a little beauty you are.'

David reckoned the combine must have been right on the point of balance and would have just about come up by hand, but who was I to argue with Jim? After all, the little grey Fergie always had been a remarkable tractor and just quietly we'd all enjoyed seeing Fred get his come-uppance.

WINTER FEEDING

When the grass grows, looking after farm stock is a doddle. All you need to do is to make sure they've enough. Well, not just enough grass, sheep eat other things as well – clover, thistles when they're young and tender, and just about anything in the garden if they get half a chance. But provided they're fat and contented, then 'checking the sheep' is a grand job on a balmy June morning and an excellent excuse for not doing the washing up.

'Are you busy this morning, dear?' It must be a universal question in thousands of farm kitchens after Sunday breakfast. You take a quick look at the pile of dishes and have a guilty twinge about digging the garden, but what you say is, 'Ah, I've just got to check the ewes and lambs in West Down. I may have to shift a few this morning, but I'll be back in time to watch the farming programme on television before lunch.' Then you beat a hasty retreat under the wife's disapproving eye to go off for a leisurely stroll with the dogs and a chat over the fence with a neighbour on the same errand.

In winter, however, it's another matter; the stock have to be fed every day regardless. My family were always pretty good about helping to 'feed out' at weekends in the winter. I used to carry seven or eight hundred breeding ewes at Netton. They'd be shut up in 'sacrifice fields' – fields that were due to be ploughed for spring cropping so that sheep constantly nibbling any grass that dared to shoot did no damage. By Christmas time the sheep would be well and truly used to dry feed – the hay and nuts that were fed to them daily. The nuts were a balanced ration of protein and carbohydrate with vitamins and minerals added, and the idea was to feed a carefully planned diet so that the sheep wouldn't get too fat. As they became increasingly pregnant the quantity of nuts could be increased as well. Fine in theory, but nobody had ever bothered to tell the ewes that too many nuts at Christmas time was bad for them; feeding-out became a pretty physical job. It was funny how quickly sheep that would rush away from you in alarm in the summer when there was plenty of grass would learn to steal nuts from your jacket pockets in the winter.

First job on Sunday would be to load the hay and nuts onto a tractor and trailer – about fifty bales and a dozen bags of nuts would be an average ration. Then I'd collect any volunteers and sling them up on top of the hay with the dogs and go off round the farm. First stop would be the rams. The old boys lived separately and there were between fifteen and twenty which lived in a small paddock next to a wood – good shelter whatever the wind direction. They were the worst to feed so I always tried to do them first. I say the worst because the Down rams I kept were very strong and very tame. Their hay rack was next to the road so I could shake out a bale of hay without going into the field; but feeding the nuts meant hopping over the fence and filling their two long wooden troughs. However you tried to do this the rams would be in the way, pushing and barging you and each other to get at the goodies. They'd take no notice of the dogs – even if Scotty gave them a nip they'd only pause to charge him before coming back to the scrum around me. What

I tried to do was to get over the fence and then run like the dickens and fill the troughs before they caught up with me. This was fine when it was dry, but when it was wet, running was impossible. Falling over among the rams with a bag of nuts was bad news, so you had to resort to a barging, swearing match until you managed to get the job done.

One old Hampshire ram I had was the very devil. He was enormous, he must have weighed close to 300 lb and stood as high as a small Shetland pony. He was called Sam, and he'd wait until I'd finished putting the nuts in the trough and turned to go. Then, whilst his mates had their heads down and I was trudging away, he'd put his head down and charge. And if you're wondering how heavy 300 lb is, I can tell you it's bigger than the biggest rugby player in the Calcutta Cup! There were only two ways to deal with Sam. If it was wet you'd have to back across the field, facing him all the way, swatting at his nose with the empty cake bag and yelling like a dervish. If it was dry I used to catch him, and, by reaching under his body for his off hind leg, 'throw' him on his side. Then I'd roll him over onto his back so that all four legs stuck straight up into the air. Then I'd run like mad for the fence. The idea was to make it before he'd managed to right himself and renew the attack.

Feeding the ewes was a great deal easier. They would be split into groups of two and three hundred, and as we came up to the first gate the 'team' would swing into action as I slowed the tractor. Scotty would be off and over the gate in a flash. His job was to keep the sheep in the field whilst whichever of my children had volunteered to come and help would hop down to open the gate. Once we were inside the field then the volunteer – usually my son Stuart – would take charge of the tractor. It's illegal now, of course, but Stuart at nine was a fine tractor driver. He knew exactly where to go and how fast, whilst he'd keep an eye out for sheep to make sure they didn't get under the trailer. This would leave me free to feed out the nuts and have a good look at the sheep at the same time. The dogs would keep the sheep out of my way whilst I filled the troughs – twenty ewes to each trough, fifteen troughs for three hundred ewes. Once the ewes were all chomping away we'd go over to fill the hay racks – fifteen or twenty bales depending on the weight of each bale. Then back to the gate and I'd become driver again to go down the road to the next flock.

It all sounds idyllic, and it was when the sun was shining. When it was pouring with rain or freezing cold, it was another matter, however. And the worst time was when it snowed.

I know that snow is pretty common in this country, but it's not on the coast in South Devon, and that Christmas we simply weren't ready for it. It had been bitterly cold all week and we'd been busy with frozen pipes and tractors that wouldn't start.

'Could snow tonight, Dan.' Preston was a great deal more reliable than any weather man, but in this case he agreed with the experts. Mind you, they were forecasting a full-scale blizzard.

'Snow?' I said. 'How bad do you reckon it'll be?'

'Trouble is the wind,' he answered. 'It'll drift badly, specially with the fields dry and frozen. There'll be nothing to hold it.'

We had a council of war. 'If we put the ewes all together in Slade Field, because of the valley it'll be sheltered whichever way the wind comes. We could take a load of hay up there this afternoon, and leave it just outside the gate, then we'll be able to feed the sheep even if the snow drifts block the road.'

'What about the young sheep?'

I was wintering 150 ewe lambs. They were supposed to be on turnips, but these had frozen solid so we'd shifted them into a grass field until things improved.

'They'll have to stay put,' I said, 'I know it's a bit exposed in Well Park but there's nowhere else to put them.'

Preston shook his head. We both knew the snow would drift. Well Park was a wide flat field.

'What about the rams?'

'We'll bring them into the sheep yards by the barn,' I said. 'They'll be easy to keep an eye on there and there's only twenty.'

'And the cliff ewes?' I has purchased two hundred odd pure Swaledale sheep from the Cumbrian fells so that we could breed our own replacements. These tough black-faced horned sheep had settled in extremely well and were doing fine on the steep gorse-clad slopes of the cliff land. We'd tried giving them a few bales of hay earlier in the week but after a cursory sniff they'd left it, preferring the coarse grass and green shoots among the gorse bushes.

'They'll just have to take pot luck,' I said. 'It's two o'clock now and it'll take until dark to organize the rest, let alone try and get them off the cliff in this weather.'

In fact the weather was getting worse all the time. It was blowing a bitterly cold gale from the north-east and the sky was full of heavy, grey-black scudding clouds. We'd finished by the time it was dark, everything fed and shifted, so Preston set off for his house two miles away.

'Come and get me if you need a hand tomorrow, Boss,' he said as he left.

'John and I'll manage,' I said. 'Don't worry.'

John lived on the farm and he and I agreed to make a start feeding out at nine in the morning. As we said goodnight and as I headed into the cheerful warmth of the kitchen it started to snow.

'Daddy! Daddy! Mummy says she can't open the back door.'

Next morning the children were wildly excited, the blizzard had come with a vengeance. Not that there had been a lot of snow, but the gale had gone on all night and created huge drifts. The back door was blocked by one four feet deep, and we had to climb out of the kitchen window to get it cleared.

'They seem fine. We'll give them a couple of extra bales in case it gets bad again tomorrow.'

John and I had had to walk across the fields to get to the ewes in Slade. The road up the hill had completely filled with snow to the height of the Devon banks on either side. The drifts were up to eight feet deep and impassable. We'd carried the hay through the gate to the ewes. They were all together on the flat top of the field in no more than two inches of snow and feeding them had been a piece of cake.

· 'Don't know about the ewe lambs, Boss,' John said. 'The drifts look bad across Well Park.'

Indeed, the ewe lambs were in a fine pickle. They'd gone in front of the blizzard until they came to the south-east corner of the field. Here, where a stone wall met a conventional Devon bank, they'd crowded into a huddle. Then the snow had blown over them covering the whole area in drifts up to five feet deep. These drifts had completely covered the wall on the southern boundary and it had been so cold that the snow was packed and frozen – hard enough so that the rearmost half of the flock had simply walked over into the next field! This lot were fine, and were simply standing waiting patiently for help.

'We'd better feed the hay, John,' I said. We'd carried a bale each across the field as we came. 'But there must be forty or fifty lambs missing. 'I'm afraid they're under these drifts.'

Indeed they were, and John and I spent the next four hours digging them out. Hard, back-breaking work, but thankfully all but two were alive and well. The two that didn't make it had been suffocated by their flock mates and were right in the corner of the field. By now it was half past two in the afternoon and already getting dark. We'd brought a couple more bales of hay across to feed the lambs and we were both physically spent. Getting the lambs out of the deep snow and the incessant punishment of the northerly gale had been tough going.

'What about the cliff ewes?' John asked. I groaned inwardly. Heaven knows what it would be like out on the cliff. It would take a good hour to get out there with some hay; that'd be half past three, and it would be dark by four.

'We'll just have to hope they've managed to stay clear of the drifts, John,' I said, hoping against hope. We'd have no chance of any major rescue operations that afternoon.

It was gone half past three when we reached the top of the

cliff. We'd managed to get across the open cornfields with the tractor and link box carrying a dozen bales of hay – more than enough to keep the ewes going, if only we could find them. Getting from the last cornfield onto the cliff proper had been a misery. I'd had to cut the fence as the gateway was blocked by yet another enormous drift, and trying to cut the wire in the ice-cold wind had been desperately slow. We drove out onto the cliff and down the slope before stopping on a small flat area, shielded from the gale by the rising ground behind us. The scene was unforgettable. The whole of the cliff was blanketed in snow – right down to the rocks by the sea. The sky was black and angry but split by weak shafts of late afternoon sun that lit the scene like something from an eighteenth-century painting.

There was a big sea running, but the waves, instead of crashing onto the rocks to send up clouds of spume, had their tops swept back by the force of the northerly gale. The wind was also sweeping away any sound of the sea pounding on the rocks, which added to the eerie feeling of watching a silent film – a scene from some Victorian tragedy at sea or an illustration from Edgar Allan Poe.

'I can't see any sheep, Boss! Do you reckon they're buried, like the lambs?'

'They shouldn't be, John, these hill ewes are supposed to know how to look after themselves.'

I tried to sound enthusiastic, but looking down and across the cliff I could see that all the pits and hollows were filled with snow, and the track that followed the contour fifty yards below us had disappeared completely in the smooth whiteness. The only features that showed were two or three odd rock outcrops and an old stone wall on the eastern slope, exposed to the wind and so swept clear of snow about a quarter of a mile away.

'They must be buried, Boss. I can't see any.' We peered into the gathering gloom. I decided to at least give the sheep a chance.

'Come UP . . . Come UP . . . Come UP . . .' I yelled as loud as I could. Nothing. 'COME UP . . . COME UP . . . Come on then . . . There! Look! There, over by the wall!' And sure enough vague shapes had begun to detach themselves from the wall on the exposed slope. 'Come on, come on, sheep, sheep, sheep . . .!'

'I'd never have believed that, Boss,' said John. 'Look! they're following that old girl in front, right across the slope.' I didn't answer but watched as the sheep came across the slope in single

file towards us, led by a single ewe picking the route and avoiding the worst drifts with the ease of a seasoned veteran. As they came, I counted: 204. Not one was missing! The ewes came right up to the tractor for their hay as though a blizzard in South Devon was no more than a storm in a teacup. By the time we left them and got back to the farm it was pitch dark and we'd both had enough.

'Thanks, John,' I said. 'We'd better be ready for another go in the morning.'

'That's all right, Boss, I'll be ready. Nine o'clock?'

'No!' I said. 'Let's make it half past. It can't be as bad as today . . .'

THE CLIFF

'Now, sir, just look at that.'

My father and I had stood beside the land agent and looked.

'Just gorse and rabbits as far as I can see,' said my father.

'Ah, yes, but look at the view, sir. Isn't it just beautiful?'
Father wasn't impressed. Setting up a son in farming had very
little to do with such niceties.

'Humph,' he said, 'precious little to be made out of a view.
Let's get on and see the better land.'

After twenty-five years I'd have to agree with both of them.
The cliff land never made much money, but it is extraordinarily
beautiful; and now it's safely in the hands of the National Trust
everyone can enjoy it. When Father bought the farm, however,
it was just about solid gorse and brambles. A hundred and thirty
acres of very steep land which gave way to quite dangerous shale
cliffs up to eighty feet high, which were incessantly pounded by
the sea. The previous owners had run a few cattle on the top of

the cliffs in a half-hearted sort of way, but I was keen to use every available acre.

'It would make some great sheep grazing if we could get rid of the gorse,' I said to Father. 'I saw thousands of acres in New Zealand just like it.'

'It's not the same here, Dan,' Father said. 'In New Zealand the soil is basically good. This land is very poor. If you get rid of the gorse it won't grow enough grass to make it worth the effort; better leave it to the rabbits.'

Well, there certainly were plenty of rabbits. When the land was part of a rich estate in the last century, they'd built a seven-foot-high stone wall right along the top of the cliff land to keep the rabbits out. My neighbour David had explained how before the war rabbits paid the rent. 'Every hundred yards or so you'll find a hole a foot square in the bottom of the wall. We'd leave these holes open for a week or so into a field that had been cut for hay, and the rabbits would come up from the cliff at night to have a good nibble at the fresh grass. Then we'd pick a good dark night and we'd set a long net the cliff side of these holes. My job would be to crouch behind the wall with a hand on the net whilst Father took the dog and a lamp. He'd drive the rabbits back towards the cliff and *whump*. You'd feel them get tangled in the net as they scampered back through the hole in the wall. As soon as I felt a rabbit hit the net I'd rush out and grab it. We'd literally catch them by the dozen and then when we'd had a couple of nights on one section of the wall we'd close these holes with slates and open up further along.'

The wall on Netton cliffs had been allowed to fall into disrepair long ago, with most of it having gone to rebuild other walls or new houses in the village. Anyway I wasn't interested in harvesting rabbits. I reckoned that despite what Father said I could reclaim the land from gorse and turn it into sheep pasture.

I had 3-400 sheep; perhaps if I let them out on top of the cliff they'd eat their way round the gorse areas and make it easier to deal with. This logic was pretty tenuous as gorse covered at least 120 of the 130 acres, and the sheep, once they'd finished the grass along the top of the gorse area, found their way down to the bottom of it just above the cliff proper. There were a few grassy flats here, too exposed for gorse or brambles, and every so often a spring ran down to the sea forming near-vertical gulleys that were covered in ivy.

'There's a couple of ewes gone over the edge after the ivy, Boss.' Ewes over the edge! That was all I needed. I played rugby in those days and had been celebrating a particularly good game the night before.

John looked at me with some concern. 'Are you sure you're all right?'

'Yes, of course I am, John,' I said.

'Shall we get the coast guard to give us a hand?' John asked. 'They're always keen to help pull up any cattle that go over.'

Get the coast guard to help with a couple of sheep? 'No need, John,' I said airily, 'you and I can manage. Now if you bring plenty of rope and an iron bar to anchor it, I'll go down the rope and tie the sheep on, then you can haul them up!' The theory sounded fine, and after taking a couple of aspirin to keep the head at bay, we set out for the cliff.

'Blowing a bit,' said John cheerfully. Blowing a bit was the understatement of the year. It was a good force 8 from the south-west, and once we'd scrambled down through the gorse to the top of the steep cliff the wind whipped our words away and the sea crashed grey and angry on the rocks 150 feet below.

'There they are. Look, down there, on that ledge!' I peered over and, sure enough, about 40 feet below us, were two sheep, heads down, standing precariously on a narrow ledge above the sea and rocks below. They'd gone down a gulley after the ivy that was 20 feet or so away from where they huddled.

'What will you do, Boss?' said John, looking at me hopefully, as though he thought I might lasso the sheep from where we stood.

'We'll get the bar in back here, John,' I said, 'it needs to be well down. Then, if we make fast the long rope, I'll toss it down. If I can get it in front of the sheep they may turn, then they might just come back up the gulley.'

John looked at me doubtfully, but he was new to sheep, having been trained on cows, so he said nothing.

'Ready, John?' I shouted against the roar of the wind.

'Yes, fine,' John said, coming forward from where he'd been tying the rope securely to the bar now a good three feet into the ground. 'You'll not get that out in a hurry!'

'Right,' I said, 'here goes.' And I threw the coils of rope out over the edge of the cliff aiming so that they would fall in front of the two animals below. The wind had other ideas, however, and a sudden gust caught the rope as it lazily uncoiled and it swirled back to land with a thumping smack like a giant snake right on top of the sheep. The result was immediate and electrifying . . . the rearmost ewe shot back, reared up . . . teetered on the ledge and then charged back to the gulley. She didn't stop at the bottom of the steep face but simply kept going like a mountain goat, straight up through the ivy to emerge a few yards from where we stood. She stood puffing and stared at us, wild-eyed for a second or two before turning to crash blindly away through the gorse up the hill.

'Blimey!' said John, 'I never thought she'd come up like that!'

To tell the truth nor had I.

The other sheep, meanwhile, had been struck on the behind by the heavy rope and had pushed forward to the very end of the ledge. She now stood poised on the sheer cliff face. The ledge was too narrow for her to turn and it looked as though she was determined to launch herself into space. I didn't bother to think but said tersely to John, 'Watch this end!' I knelt, grabbed the rope and slid down over the edge of the cliff. When I reached the ledge I saw just how narrow it was. The sheep was no more than four feet to my right, and as I leant out from the cliff, feet on the ledge, holding the rope for support to get a better view of the situation, the sheep must have sensed me behind her and I saw her rear legs bunch ready to spring. I swung sideways, and, grabbing her by the wool over her shoulders, pulled her backwards towards me. The ewe reared up on her back legs and gave a convulsive heave which just about sent us both crashing down to the rocks below. Desperately I swung her out in front of me and *plonk* . . . I wound up sitting on the ledge with the ewe like some ungainly poodle on my lap – but at least her legs were away from the cliff.

'Well, old girl,' I panted in her ear, 'what now?' What now indeed. Like a fool I'd come down without any extra lengths of string to tie the ewe's legs, and so in the end I had to tie her up with the rope itself. After a struggle I had her securely lashed and I yelled for John to haul her up. He'd been watching the performance from safety above, peering over the edge, and he soon got the idea and began heaving away. The ewe struggled and bounced against the cliff, but the knots held and she gradually disappeared upwards, leaving me sitting on the ledge.

It took John what seemed an age to get the ewe up and find some string to make her safe. I waited, sitting a hundred feet above the crashing sea with the wind tugging at my coat. As the adrenalin subsided my hangover returned, and after five minutes or so I was feeling thoroughly miserable. I vowed I'd reclaim the cliff properly, clear the gorse and put up a proper fence along the top of the worst rocky places. I didn't fancy spending every Sunday morning at the end of a rope . . .

Reclamation

To make a start on the reclamation it seemed a good idea to swale the gorse. Swaling is a rural term that means having a controlled burn, but trying to have a controlled burn of gorse is a bit like cleaning off petrol pumps with a blow torch; very difficult for things not to get out of hand.

I'd started off one Saturday morning in March with the idea of just burning twenty acres or so to see how it went. But the gorse seeds are full of oil and it went like a raging inferno – so well, in fact, that to save a major incident I had to 'back burn' at the eastern end of the cliff to prevent the fire I'd started at the western end heading for Torquay twenty miles or so down the coast. So in the event the whole cliff burned off, all 120 acres of it. The gorse bushes lost all their leaves, flowers and dead prickles of last year's growth and were left as black spindly skeletons with the stringy tough branches covered in a fine layer of charcoal. 'Great,' I thought, 'that's really opened things up. Now the sheep'll be able to get amongst things.' They certainly were, and when we'd had some rain and the cliff had greened up a bit, the ewes eagerly pushed in amongst the skeletal gorse bushes looking for tender shoots of grass, so that within a few days the whole flock were as black as chimney sweeps!

Unfortunately sheep are not like goats: they much prefer grass to gorse regrowth. Within three months every gorse bush had a vigorous 'beard' of young growth, fully rejuvenated by the fire and ready to re-establish control. By the next year in late spring the worst patches were as impenetrable as ever, with nettles, thistles and brambles fighting for what little space the gorse had left. I decided it was time for Plan B.

About fifteen acres next to the camp site was not quite as steep as the rest and just the ticket for Plan B; we'd 'swipe' off the gorse and brambles, then plough and re-seed it – simple as that! I'd found a good keen man who was willing to plough and re-seed the land if I got it 'swiped' off.

'You don't think it's too steep?' I asked Roy the contractor.

'No, sir,' laughed Roy, ''tis nowhere near as steep as the last piece we've done. Won't even need dual wheels on the tractors.'

I looked down the slope. It was pretty steep and the gorse was up to seven feet tall here, the land protected from the south-west wind by a rocky promontory a quarter of a mile away.

'Must be reasonable soil, look at all the bracken,' Roy said. 'Anyone knows bracken means good soil.' Roy could sense I was losing a bit of my enthusiasm for the job.

'Right,' I agreed, annoyed by my own indecision. 'We'll have a go. If it's good soil it's a shame to have it growing rubbish like this.'

It's just as well there weren't so many environmentalists

about in those days, but David Bellamy was still an obscure teacher somewhere up north and you could still get away with calling entangled wilderness 'rubbish'.

'You'll get it swiped off, then?' said Roy, forcing the pace. 'I could get down in a fortnight.'

'Ah . . . well, yes . . . OK . . . two weeks, we'll get it done then.'

A couple of days later John and I were back out on the cliff ready for swiping off. I'd fitted dual wheels on one of the tractors and put the front wheels out to match. This made the machine nine feet wide and we'd had to take a fence down to get out on to the cliff top because the gates were too narrow. On the back of the tractor was the swipe – a simple tool like a very large Flymo driven by the tractor power take off. Under a heavy steel canopy were a pair of murderous two-foot-long hinged steel blades that would chop up trees as thick as a man's leg and send stones shooting a hundred yards – not an outfit to stand behind, but great for the job in hand.

'Where will you start then?' John asked.

'Oh, I'll try a couple of swathes along the top, then I'll cut a strip out top to bottom,' I said airily. The cliff waited, silent and steep.

The swipe was perfect for the job and I'd trimmed the flatter land on top in no time. It was quite extraordinary to drive into clumps higher than the tractor and see them come out as small pieces of pulp behind. Here goes nothing, I thought, and, pointing the tractor downhill, drove down into the jungle. Within an hour I was tackling the steepest bits with exhilaration. The dual wheels and extra wide set-up on the tractor made child's play of the slopes.

After two hours I handed over to John. 'Just keep to second low gear,' I said, 'sixteen hundred revs, and if it's really big stuff go over it twice.'

'Right, Boss,' said John, as eager as anything to have a go himself. After watching him get the feel of the job I left him to it. 'Cracked it . . .' I thought, 'we'll do this piece this year, and next year we'll have a go at the big piece next door – a good 40 acres there – by the time it's all re-seeded it'll carry an extra 150 ewes. That would pay for the whole operation in less than two seasons.' I couldn't wait to tell my father.

Roy came and did a fantastic job ploughing down all the trash, then discing and rolling . . . discing and rolling . . . until he got a seed-bed fine enough to plant a mixture of rape and grass seeds. The change was quite extraordinary. Within four weeks the bare slopes were covered in tender thrusting green. Within two months I'd put a bunch of lambs on to the new growth and they were fattening as you watched them.

'What do you think, David?' I asked my neighbour. He'd been interested to see the progress as he'd even more cliff land than I had and was going to have a go at reclamation as well.

'I'm not sure, Dan,' he said, 'I don't think there's much top soil on these old cliffs. I'm just a bit worried that ploughing them up is wrong, somehow. The only goodness must be in the top inch or so, and to bury that seven or eight inches down – but I must say, it does look good at the moment.'

We stood looking down at the steep green slope dotted with healthy fattening lambs.

By the following spring David's doubts about the wisdom of ploughing seemed sadly correct. The soil was poor, and, despite my having put on more lime and chemical fertilizer, some balance of trace elements was missing. The rye grass and clover that had started so well was now barely 25 per cent of the pasture, and Bent, Yorkshire Fog, thistles, and here and there little clumps of gorse seedlings, were appearing. David had been right. We'd have to get rid of the gorse without ploughing.

It was time for Plan C, and I decided to try a spray to kill the gorse that had been successful in New Zealand called 2.4.5.T. (which is now banned).

'What we'll do is to swipe off the gorse first, John. Then, when it re-grows, we'll spray the re-growth. It'll be impossible to tackle the stuff as it is now.'

The gorse varied in height a good deal. Where it was protected from the south-west it grew to six or seven feet high, but where it was exposed to the wind it was low and dense. We'd have to spray it by hand to get every plant covered, and unless we swiped it down to size, that would be totally impractical.

'Righto, Boss,' said John. And for the next few weeks he spent every hour he could spare from regular farm work on the cliff swiping the gorse.

Disaster struck one Monday morning. 'It's in the sea! I'm sorry, Boss. It must have been a bit slippery!' John stood in my office white and still a bit shaky.

'Well, thank goodness you're OK,' I said. 'Now tell me what's happened.'

John had been turning the tractor and swipe just above an inlet called Bloody Cove, when he'd felt the tractor start to slide down the steep slope towards the sheer cliffs. He hadn't waited to argue but had baled out immediately to watch the tractor slide ten yards or so. The gorse had concealed a raft of shale exposed on the surface which had stopped the tyres on the tractor from gripping. When we got out to the scene of the accident, it was clear from the tyre marks what had happened. The tractor had slid into the fence we'd erected to keep the sheep away from Bloody Cove and stopped, but John had left it in gear. Throttle set, the powerful engine had driven the machine forward through the fence and out over the edge. It had fallen eighty feet down the sheer cliff to crash down onto a rock amongst the waves below. The result had been quite devastating. All the tyres had burst with the force of the impact. The radiator and well over half the engine had been smashed to smithereens. The back axle had ruptured in two places.

'Well!' I said. 'That's that!'

The only thing worth saving on the tractor itself was the tool box. The swipe was another matter, however. Cushioned from the full force of the impact by the link arms of the tractor it had survived with only a couple of dents in its tough steel canopy. It seemed that something might be salvaged from the disaster but we'd need to get it out of Bloody Cove. After losing one tractor I wasn't too keen on the idea of trying to haul it back up the cliff, but David and I shared a sixteen-foot fishing boat. Perhaps if we lashed the swipe to empty barrels we could tow it round to the village harbour a couple of miles up the coast? Anything was better than sitting and thinking what might have happened to John if he hadn't jumped off, so we tackled the project with enthusiasm.

'Right then, Dan. That should do it.' David had come to help and was at the helm of *Marcelle*, our converted lifeboat.

'OK,' I said. 'John – you hold her steady until we take up the slack.'

It had taken much longer than we'd thought to get the swipe extracted from the tractor and lashed to oil drums, so that it was late in the afternoon now and the bright sunny weather had given way to ominous grey clouds scudding up the channel from the south-west.

'I don't like the look of the weather, Dan,' said David. 'We'll need to get a move on. It'll take a couple of hours to get back to the village.'

I looked at the angry sky and a gust of wind whipped up the waves in Bloody Cove. 'Off we go, then,' I said, and the boat moved out towards the open sea taking up the slack on the stout tow rope. For the first hundred yards or so our progress was steady, if a bit slow. John, having seen us off, had already trudged off up the cliff to disappear. He was to have his tea and then come down to the village to meet us later. We turned westwards heading into the freshening wind and choppy sea.

'I don't like it, Dan!' said David. 'We'll be here all night at this rate. In fact, I don't think we're making any headway at all.' I looked at the shore. He was right. The swipe was too much for *Marcelle* as it lay heavy in the water, and we were being carried by the tide back towards the rocks of Stoke Point further east.

'We'll have to leave it, Dan,' David said. 'There's nothing else for it. Let's anchor the swipe. This rough weather will blow through tonight and we can come and have another go in the morning.'

It certainly was blowing up, and by the time we got back to the village the sea was really rough. 'I'm glad to be out of that lot!' said David, grimacing as he tied *Marcelle* up to her moorings. 'Let's have a pint on the way home. Look, there's John with the truck, waiting.'

First thing in the morning I nipped out to the cliffs to check on the swipe. The weather was bright and fresh, and the sea sparkled, comely in the sunshine, but the anchored machine had disappeared without trace – oil drums and all!

'I reckon it was washed over to France,' John said later. 'It was pretty rough last night.'

I had real problems with the insurance claim – was I right to say we'd tried to salvage the swipe? Could I describe the tractor as having exploded on impact? In the end they sent an assessor down from London complete with Homburg hat, rolled umbrella and black shiny shoes.

'It's a fair walk down to Bloody Cove,' I said, 'especially in this weather.'

The insurance man eyed me coldly, ignoring the rain lashing my office window. 'It will be no trouble, Mr Cherrington, but I do need to see the . . . er . . . "wreck" of your tractor, sir. If it's still there, of course . . .' The innuendo hung in the air between us.

'OK,' I said, losing any sympathy I'd had for the insurance man's posh clothing. 'But I don't think I've got any spare wellies . . .'

'They won't be necessary,' said the assessor, sure he'd found a real fraud at last. 'Can we go now?'

'Sure,' I said. 'The tide should be out far enough to get right down to the wreck.'

An hour later I stood in a tidal pool beside the back axle, gear box and crank case: all that remained of the tractor. The assessor was perched on a rock a few yards away looking miserable –

his shoes sodden and ruined, umbrella wrecked by the wind hanging loosely at his side and rain dripping off the rim of his hat.

'I see,' he said. 'It really did explode, didn't it? I must agree.' He sighed deeply, 'A total write-off.'

It took nearly ten years of spraying and stocking with sheep at just the right time of the year to get on top of the gorse, but in the end I felt I'd won. The land would never be the best, I knew, but it was satisfying to walk along at lambing time to see the whole 130 acres of grassy slopes with just the odd patch of yellow gorse showing on the rocky promontories. It wouldn't carry a lot of stock, but even so, it gave a most satisfying feeling to have beaten nature and tamed the land.

In 1976 the gorse got its own back. I should have listened to Father in the first place. 1976 was the year when we had a terrible drought that went on, and on, and on. Blistering endless days with no rain for months, and the cliffs burned brown and then bleached white. The only green on the whole 130 acres were the few clumps of gorse I'd left. When the drought broke, the real damage became apparent – all the grasses we'd encouraged and nurtured over ten years or more were dead. Literally cooked on the thin rocky soil, so that when it rained, all that grew were weeds, and thousands and thousands of gorse seedlings!

After the drought my heart wasn't really in the battle with the gorse. Deep down I knew it had been a foolish venture. I kept it at bay on the best fifty acres or so, but the vast majority is now yellow with flowering gorse every spring. All signs of my efforts have disappeared, and as it is now in the hands of the National Trust, I don't suppose it will ever be disturbed again.

ENTERTAINING

It's funny how often things just sort of happen when you live on a farm. Having a couple of people for supper often turns into a dozen . . .

I'd arranged to go fishing with an old mate of mine from university days called Ian. Ian wasn't a farmer, he had a high-powered job in Cornwall in fact, but we were both keen fishermen. We arranged to go salmon fishing on the Tamar. I didn't expect the fishing to be much good as it was too early in the season, but it was a beautiful place to be and we'd have a fine chance to reminisce on the old days. We'd arranged to go on a Friday and Ian rang me on the previous Sunday evening.

'Dan! How are you?' he started.

'Ian! . . . now don't say you can't make it on Friday – it's all arranged!' I knew Ian of old. He was always too busy.

'No, no, it's not that, Dan. Look, I've got a couple of blokes coming down from London. Would it be too much to ask . . . could they come too?'

'Of course,' I said, 'but we can only fish with one rod . . . would they mind taking turns?'

'Oh, I'm sure they'll just enjoy seeing the river. Look, that's great, Dan. What chance of a fish do you think?'

★

Ian rang again on Monday. 'Dan . . .'

'Ian! Good to hear you again. What can I do for you?'

'Well, funny you should mention that, Dan,' said Ian. 'Look, you know I'm involved with ship repairing . . . well, those blokes I was telling you about are actually Russians.'

'Well, that's OK,' I said, 'I'm not anti-Russian or anything.'

'No, no,' laughed Ian, 'I'm sure you're not. But, look . . . they're very keen to see a bit of real English country life . . . er . . . good old farm cooking and all that! Would there be any chance of giving them supper on Thursday? I'd bring the booze . . .' he added quickly. Well, I thought, why not? 'Look, Ian,' I said, 'you'd better hang on, I'll need to ask Sandy.'

'Er . . . look,' I said to Sandy, 'you know Ian and I are going fishing on Friday. Would it be OK if he and a couple of chaps came to supper on Thursday . . . nothing special, they'd be quite happy to take pot luck?'

'Fine,' said Sandy. 'How many?'

'Three altogether,' I said gratefully. I'd explain they were Russians later. She'd be interested to meet real live Russians.

Ian rang again on Wednesday. 'Dan. Look, could we possibly make it five on Thursday? I'm sorry about this.'

Five! I asked Sandy. 'Five?' she said, 'Yes, I suppose so. I'll need to organize some extra food, though.'

On Thursday morning Ian came clean. 'Look, Dan,' he said, 'I couldn't explain before because of security. It's actually the Russian Ambassador and his party who are making an official tour of the south-west. He asked for an informal evening. I thought . . .' Ian trailed off.

The Russian Ambassador! 'How many in his party?' I asked Ian.

'Er . . . ten altogether. Well, eleven, counting me! And that's everybody,' he said quickly.

'Eleven! Hell, Ian, what am I supposed to say to Sandy?'

'Look, Sandy,' I said, 'Ian's party is going to be a few more . . and . . . one of the Russians is . . er . . . the Ambassador.

There'll be eleven altogether! But they just want something simple!'

Sandy was a bit cross. 'Eleven! Really, what on earth am I supposed to feed them on?'

'I could go off and get a ham,' volunteered Pat, my secretary, 'and I'll help you get things ready . . .'

'We'll need . . .' As Sandy took over, turning the crisis into normality, I slunk out of the house.

'It's lucky the weather's good,' said Sandy at seven o'clock. And indeed it was a fine spring evening. 'Can you keep them outside for an hour or so? We're not quite ready yet.'

'Right,' I said, 'I'll take them on a tour of the farm.' With that, we heard cars approaching and the guests arrived. Well, the police cars arrived first, then the Russian Ambassador's Bentley. Then his bodyguard, then Ian's car. Then more police cars. The police vanished to surround the farm. Sandy shot off into the kitchen.

'At least an hour,' she said.

Ian led the party in through the back gate. 'Hullo, Dan,' he said, 'This . . .' I shook hands with everybody as we stood in the yard outside the back door.

'Ah, well, welcome to Netton,' I said to the Ambassador, who was rather short, immaculately dressed, and looked a bit like Hercule Poirot. 'I thought perhaps you might like to have a look around the farm a bit . . . mm . . . you know, stretch your legs?'

A very large, very tough-looking Russian with a heavy weather-beaten face standing beside the Ambassador stared at me grimly.

'Or perhaps you'd like a drink first?' I finished lamely.

'We drink!' said the large Russian, and he set off purposefully towards the back door.

'Will that be all right?' asked a very smooth-looking PR sort of person with gloves and a silk scarf . . . and he guided us into the house. Sandy looked none too pleased as we traipsed through the kitchen. I shrugged and said, 'Er . . . we're going to have a drink!'

'Whisky or gin,' I asked, 'or I've got a couple of cans of beer?'

'Whisky,' said the very large Russian. 'I am the Trade Commissionaire, my name is Igor!'

Igor went over to the sideboard and picked up my only bottle of whisky. 'Ha,' he said, 'Bells!' With that he took off the cap and tossed it into the fireplace. He then proceeded to empty the bottle into half a dozen glasses which he passed round to his fellow Russians except the Ambassador, who asked for a small gin and tonic.

'Where is vodka?' demanded Igor.

'Here,' said Ian, appearing from the rear of the group. Ian grinned at me, obviously enjoying himself hugely. He gave Igor a bottle of vodka. Igor poured a good quarter pint into a beer glass and handed it to me.

'You drink vodka!' he said.

Because supper wasn't quite ready we went on drinking for a while. Ian produced more whisky, but Igor made me stick to vodka. After the first couple of glasses I got quite keen on it and found the Rusian Ambassador quite easy to talk to. He and I and the smooth PR man stood by the living room window looking out into the small paddock next to the sheep yards. The paddock was only about an acre and it was full of ewe lambs waiting for a worm drench in the morning.

'How big is this field?' asked the PR man.

'One acre,' I said.

'How many sheep do you keep in it?' he asked – of course he meant how many on average for the year, but I answered unthinkingly, 'Just over a hundred,' meaning the ewe lambs parked there over night.

'That is RUBBISH,' said the Ambassador, looking me sternly in the eye. 'A wildly exaggerated claim . . .' And before I could explain he wandered off.

Dinner arrived and we all sat down. Igor sat next to me whilst the PR man and the Ambassador sat next to Sandy at the other end of the table.

'More vodka?' said Igor. My head was swimming a bit so I said, 'No thanks, Igor. It's jolly good stuff though.'

'Ha! You try brandy now!' He then produced a bottle of Armenian brandy and poured about a third of it into my glass. Filling his own glass to the brim with neat whisky, he said, 'Now, we drink!' And giving me a nudge which rattled my back teeth, he tossed his whisky down in one!

'Ha!' I said, fired up by the vodka, 'we DRINK.' And I tossed down the Armenian brandy . . .

I can well understand why Armenian brandy isn't a big seller in this country – neat methylated spirits is probably a bit smoother! Tears came to my eyes and I lost the power of speech for a while.

Igor was concerned. 'Ha,' he said, 'you are not well? You need a DRINK . . . Here, have more brandy . . .'

The meal passed by in a strange haze. Russians have a different way of doing things to us. Sandy brought in the trout that had been the original supper for ourselves, Ian and a 'couple of friends'. She offered the dish to Igor to help himself.

'Ha!' he said. 'Trout?' And tipped the lot onto his plate . . .

I offered a bowl of peas to the Russian Ambassador's chauffeur. Well, he drove the car but he was a pretty tough-looking character. He nodded and smiled, and tipped that bowlful onto his plate! Sandy disappeared into the kitchen . . . Miraculously, more food appeared and eventually a satisfied buzz of conversation went round the table. Ian lifted his glass to me and grinned his thanks. I made the mistake of taking another slug of Armenian brandy. The smooth PR man was telling Sandy about life in Russia.

'In Russia we go fishing in moving huts . . . In the middle of the winter, we cut a hole in the ice in the middle of the hut, then we fish through the floor and drink vodka . . .' Igor was explaining how Moscovites fished in winter.

'Excuse me, Mr Cherrington.' It was the smooth PR man. 'The Ambassador would be very grateful if he could watch the BBC news on the television. He likes to keep in touch.'

'Of course, of course,' I said. I weaved my way over to the television set and switched on. It was bang on nine o'clock. The Russians all left the table and came to gather round the television. The Cold War was going strong at that time and the first item was our Prime Minister, Margaret Thatcher, being the Iron Lady. She was thumping the table at some dinner or other telling the world and its wife that we could NEVER – NEVER kowtow to the ill-mannered bullying tactics of the Russian Bear!

The Ambassador looked most unhappy and started talking quietly to himself. The smooth PR man turned off the television set . . . 'Thank you for the excellent dinner, Mr Cherrington. Now we must go . . .'

'Not yet, surely,' I protested. I was beginning to get a taste for the Armenian brandy!

'Ha,' said Igor, 'we go now? But tomorrow we FISH . . . and then we DRINK!' And with that they left.

Next morning I woke up late with the most dreadful hangover!

'Serves you right,' said Sandy, 'aren't you supposed to take them fishing?'

I looked at my watch. Hell, I was already an hour late. I had arranged to meet the party at their hotel just north of Plymouth and it took about forty minutes to drive there from Netton. By the time I turned off the main road onto the quiet by-way for the last couple of miles, I was feeling utterly miserable. I vowed never to drink anything ever again! Then, as I came around a corner the road was blocked by a blue van and several large policemen were waving me to stop. One of them was speaking into a walkie-talkie. I stopped and wound the window down.

'Mr Cherrington?' the one with the walkie-talkie said. I nodded. 'You're expected, sir. Sorry to stop you, but there's been a bomb scare. The Russian party are waiting for you now!'

I drove on to the hotel to be greeted by Ian looking a bit anxious.

'Thank heaven you're here, Dan,' he said, 'they're getting a bit restive! We'd only just got here last night when there was a phone call to say someone had planted a bomb. We've been up most of the night. The Ambassador's a bit worried.'

'Do you want to call it off then?' I said hopefully.

'No . . . No . . .' said Ian, 'they're very keen to go. Can you lead off?'

The bit of the Tamar we were fishing on is very quiet and very beautiful. By the time we got there the party had grown a bit – no doubt because of the bomb scare – and we had three or four extra policemen, a couple of them important looking with peaked hats and silver pips. We got out by the river and the chauffeur pulled a table out of the back of the Bentley and began to lay it up for lunch. We all milled around and I tried to explain the intricacies of salmon fishing to the Ambassador. He clam-

bered onto a rock on the side of a large pool but didn't attempt to cast a fly across the swirling fishy-looking current. Instead, he put the tip of the rod with about two feet of gut and the fly dangling from the end of it into the water and stirred it around for a bit as though he was making porridge. After about five minutes he clambered back up the bank and handed me the rod.

'No fish,' he said.

The gillie who looked after the river was called Horace, and I'd warned him that I might have a couple of friends with me that day. As the Ambassador decided he had had enough salmon fishing for the day, Horace turned up in his battered old Land

Rover. What on earth he thought – faced with immaculate policemen, Russians in dark overcoats and fur hats and all – I don't know, but Horace had been dealing with all sorts on the river for yonks. He was used to dukes and lords, so nothing fazed him much. He got out of the Land Rover.

'Hello, Mr Cherrington.'

Ha, I thought. I was a bit in awe of Horace to tell the truth.

'Er, Horace . . . This is the Russian Ambassador from London . . . and this is Igor the Trade Commissioner!'

Horace's mouth fell open, but nothing came out.

'Ha,' said Igor, when I explained who Horace was, 'you drink!' And he handed Horace a half pint of vodka which he'd had on ice in the back of the Bentley. I tried to refuse to join them on the grounds that I was driving but one of the important looking policemen said, 'Please do, Mr Cherrington. It's important that these chaps are happy – the bomb scare wasn't good news.' I glanced at the mammoth glassful in the policeman's hand and shrugged. Oh well, I thought, at least it's not the Armenian brandy!

The party got well under way and Ian and I spent a while teaching the chauffeur how to cast a fly line. The Russian Ambassador, however, had other things on his mind. He spent the time looking deeply worried – hands clasped behind his back, head down, walking to and fro along a two-hundred-yard section of the river bank. Unfortunately his perambulations took on the appearance of a rather hysterical farce. No doubt he had the worries of the world on his shoulders, but as he walked he was followed by two of his own bodyguards, and then two police constables, to protect His Excellency against attack I suppose. Each time the Ambassador turned to walk pensively back over his chosen beat, the bodyguard and the policemen would dive into the bushes so as not to disturb his deliberations; as he passed then they would emerge, looking a bit dishevelled from the bracken and brambles, to fall in behind at a discreet but protective distance. The effect was that instead of the emissary of one of the world's mightiest powers, the little figure of the Ambassador looked more like Peter Sellers taking off the King of Ruritania . . . But then the whole episode still seems slightly unreal. The only thing it did do for certain was to put me off Armenian brandy for ever.

RAMS

It's no good keeping ewes if you haven't got the rams to go with them. There's a good deal of folklore and mystery surrounding rams; according to breeders who sell them you need one ram for every thirty or so ewes in the flock. I've always thought this was overdoing things a bit, but, of course, if you're selling it's good to convince shepherds that it's better to be safe than sorry. 'Two to fight and one to work,' John Toms, my father's old foreman, used to say, but what it comes down to at the end of the day is just how keen the old boys are on the job in hand.

The New Zealanders are great ones for efficiency and saving cash, and I remember an experiment that was carried out on one of their research farms. A ram was tethered to the fence in a large field with a hundred ewes, and he successfully served the whole lot! When I quoted this to David he laughed.

'Must have been his after-shave, Dan! Trouble is, some rams work and others don't. When you're buying them you never know which one is going to really get on with the job.'

True enough; it certainly has nothing to do with the price you pay. The most expensive ram I ever bought cost several hundred pounds, and that was more than twenty years ago. He was a real aristocrat with a proper name and all: 'Something or other the Sixth'. (It's not that I can't remember the name exactly, it's just that you have to be a bit careful how you talk about these things; even after twenty years!) I took the auctioneer's advice and insured 'Fred', as we'll call him for short.

'This will cover you for every contingency, Mr Cherrington: whether the ram dies or simply refuses to work, you get your money back in full.'

The vendor also 'stood behind' his little beauty. 'If he won't serve a ewe, just let me know, Mr Cherrington. I'll replace him, or you can send him back. Whichever you wish.'

Reassured by these guarantees, and by bidding enough to buy a decent second-hand tractor, I returned to Netton with my prize. I'd set about breeding my own flock and be free of the vagaries of the auction market.

In due course the breeding season arrived and Fred was put in with his selected harem – forty of the best ewes I had, in a quiet secluded paddock. Off he went, head back and upper lip curling as he sniffed the inviting aromas. To see if a ram is working when he's put out with the ewes we used to put a mixture of grease and marker dye called raddle on his chest. In the morning the tell-tale colour would show on the behind of any ewe that had been 'raddled'. Sure enough, the next morning two of the ewes had been marked by Fred. I was a bit disappointed as I'd expected five or six on the first day, if he'd been really keen. I looked around the paddock. There was Fred, sitting under an old pear tree chewing the cud with a contemplative air, surrounded by half a dozen ewes. Sitting down! With half a dozen real beauties like that! Why wasn't Fred up and at it? I walked across and he rose slowly on to his feet. The ewes shuffled around coyly, but he took no notice at all!

And that was that. Whatever I tried, or the ewes did, Fred just smiled politely and wandered off with a glazed look in his eye. I suppose, in human terms, he'd tried it and preferred to be a bachelor! I checked the insurance policy – invalid – he had served some ewes, hadn't he? It was the same with the breeder who suggested that if I'd looked after Fred better he might have showed more enthusiasm.

Mind you, Fred was better than the bunch of rams I bought for Richard, one of my neighbours. I used to deal in sheep a bit, and because I went to a fair few auctions, farmers who were too busy working to lean over the hurdles at the side of a ring for hours would commission me to buy a ram or two for them. In Richard's case it was three – Down rams for fat lamb production, and I bought him three from the same flock – all young and keen for action as far as I could see.

'Er, I say, Dan,' Richard had some trouble getting to the point on the telephone a few weeks later. 'It's these rams you bought.'

'What's wrong, Richard? Is one dead? Have they been fighting one another?'

Richard was glad of the opening. 'It's not that they're fighting, Dan, they seem to be extremely fond of one another!'

'Ah,' I said, 'that's pretty common with healthy virile rams. They often practise on each other before you put them with the ewes. Don't worry, it just shows they're keen.'

'I see,' said Richard, 'I hope you're right, Dan. But we'll soon find out. They're due to go out tomorrow, so we'll soon know.'

The day after tomorrow, Richard rang me back. 'It's the rams, I'm afraid,' he said apologetically. 'I raddled them well and put them out with the ewes. But . . .' he paused, and coughed in an embarrassed way. 'Look, could you come over and have a look?'

Well. I didn't know what to say! We stood in the field looking at the three rams, by themselves in a corner of the field. They were smothered in raddle, and the ewes were grazing well apart, obviously ignoring the activity.

'Look, I'll get the vet to have a look at them. In the meantime I'll lend you a couple of my old boys to be going on with.'

Tony, the vet, dropped in to see me at the end of the week. 'I've never seen anything like that before,' he grinned. 'They're as queer as coots! I've tested them and there's no reason why they shouldn't work – they just prefer their own company!'

'Hell,' I said, 'that's bad news. How can I get my money back? The breeder will think I'm trying one on!'

'I've thought of that,' said Tony. 'That's why I dropped in. Look, here's a letter from me saying they're homosexual – it might help.'

I must say it worked a treat. I sidled up to the breeder at the next ram sale.

'Look, I've a problem with three of your rams – won't work – prefer each other.' He began to fob me off in disbelief until I gave him a copy of Tony's letter (official, and on the vet's headed paper). The breeder read it twice.

'Ah,' he said, 'I think I'd rather give you your money back, Mr Cherrington, rather than exchange the rams. In twenty-five years this has never happened to me before. It must be something to do with the climate in South Devon.'

Over the years I gradually paid less and less money for rams. The ones that cost the most were seldom the best workers; and as I only used them to breed fat lambs it didn't seem to make much difference whether their ears were 4″ or 6″ long – not that every bargain worked out either.

'What do you think of him then?' I asked David. He peered in the back of my old farm van at the heavy looking Suffolk in the back. The Suffolk snorted and charged the door.

'Wow! He's certainly keen, Dan. How much did he cost?'

'Just five pounds!' I said proudly. 'He was right at the end of the auction amongst the old ewes and nobody else was there to bid. I reckon he's every bit as good as the pedigree rams I paid fifty pounds each for last Friday.' David agreed with me. 'It's funny how little you can buy a ram for secondhand. Too many people get fooled by the way the breeders "get them up",' he said.

I took my new acquisition down to the small field to join the other rams – always a tricky time putting a new ram amongst the residents. They'd usually have a good old shoving and charging match, and all too often a good ram would be damaged in some way – hurt his leg or something like that – and be no use for work.

The Suffolk stood his ground and let the dozen or so pedigree purchases sniff and push him around for ten minutes or so. Then they seemed to settle, and I turned and climbed the fence to walk back towards the farm. I paused to look back only to see the Suffolk squared away to the biggest Down ram I had. He pawed the ground, then backed off ten yards or so . . .

'Stop that, you stupid old sod,' I shouted, and began to run back down the hill . . . Too late. The Suffolk lowered his head and charged . . . The Down ram merely set himself, not moving . . . *crash* . . . The Down shook his head and grunted . . . The Suffolk slipped to his knees and rolling over kicking, onto his side. I reached him panting . . . the eyes were glazing over . . . he'd broken his neck clean as a whistle.

'Bad luck, but I'm not surprised,' said David when I told him my misfortune. 'I thought he looked too cheap to be true!'

HOT AIR

One thing about the countryside, it's very difficult to get it into perspective unless you're on top of a hill; or better still in an aeroplane. A series of disjointed fields and crops then becomes a pattern. If you get high enough the pattern begins to repeat itself, individual farms with similar crops forming the basic bits of a larger puzzle. Like most other farms Netton has been photographed from the air. It's easy to work out the date as the combine that caught fire is in the farmyard; the picture still fascinates me – I know it's real because I can recognize all the things in it: sheep, farmhouse, trees in the garden, junk by the machinery shed – but they are so still and toy-like that it's like a children's picture. If you fly over farmland in an aeroplane it's better; things do move below you; being in an aeroplane, however, is very noisy and, shut in this noisy box, you are cut off from reality. To get a proper bird's eye view you need to go up in a balloon.

I had a chance to do that, thanks to the BBC. It happened this way. I was sitting idly in my office one day wondering what came next when the phone rang.

'Could I speak to Dan Cherrington, please?' this rather keen, natty, cultivated voice said.

'Speaking,' I said.

'Oh, jolly good. Look, my name's Brian. I work for BBC radio. We're doing a series of programmes from a hot air balloon . . . looking at different aspects of life from the air. We're planning to do one on farming. Would you be willing to take part? I'm afraid it's not very well paid . . .'

Paid to go up in a balloon! I couldn't believe my luck. 'I'll go,' I said. 'I'll go.'

'Oh, jolly good,' said Brian.

We discussed the best place for a trip. 'Well,' I said, 'I don't think Netton's quite the place. There's a fifty per cent chance that we'd end up in France if we actually made it!'

'Yes,' said Brian, when I explained where Netton was. 'I see! Where do you suggest then?'

I thought about it. Somewhere to look at real British farming; traditional good land. 'What about Herefordshire?' I suggested.

'That would be fine,' said Brian. 'It's closer to Bristol than you are. It'll make it a bit of an early start for you, though.'

Brian explained that you only 'flew' in a balloon if conditions were right. We'd be going up in May. We'd need to be finished by nine o'clock in the morning. 'When it gets hot later in the day the thermals make it difficult to land.'

I'd been so keen to get up in a balloon I'd never bothered to think of how you get down. Oh well, it was too late to worry about that now.

'It means meeting before dawn, I'm afraid,' said Brian, 'about half-past three should be OK!'

To hell with the hour – a balloon was a balloon! 'Fine,' I said. 'Just give me a ring and I'll be there.'

Brian rang late one evening about two weeks later. 'Tomorrow looks OK, Dan, can you meet us at half-past three on the roundabout just before you cross the river Wye on the way into Hereford itself?'

I left Devon at half-past midnight and arrived in Hereford bang on half-past three. It was still dark. There, on the side of the road, was a Land Rover and trailer, a small Ford car and a group of people. I stopped, a bit disappointed at the lack of a balloon. I knew that you had to blow them up, but somehow I'd expected something bigger. As I got out and walked up to the group, I saw that the trailer behind the Land Rover was literally a big basket sitting on a flat-wheeled trolley.

'Ah, hello,' said a clean-faced, well dressed young man, detaching himself from the group. 'I'm Brian. You must be Dan.' Not waiting for a reply he introduced me to the rest of the group. 'This is Hugh. He'll be asking you questions.' Hugh nodded: he had humorous eyes, grey hair and an untidy old sweater. 'And this is Joe who flies the balloon, and his team,' Brian continued. Joe was a Midlander, down-to-earth and no messing. You felt instinctively that if you were to take off in a balloon, then Joe would be the one to go with. He shook hands.

Brian turned to Joe. 'Right,' he said, 'we're all here. Ready to go. Er . . . where are we taking off from?' Brian tailed off expectantly.

'Don't know yet,' said Joe.

'Don't know!' said Brian. 'But . . .'

'No point in arranging anything before the day,' said Joe lugubriously, 'never know which way the wind'll be blowing!'

'What do we do then?' asked Brian anxiously.

'Oh, we'll just drive around a bit and find somewhere!' said Joe. 'You follow us. OK?'

And with that Joe and his team hopped into the Land Rover and got going.

'Ah, right, Dan, you come with us, will you?' said Brian. And we took off up the road in hot pursuit.

'I do hope Joe finds somewhere,' said Brian, as we followed the swaying trailer through the narrow Herefordshire lanes.

'Perhaps a common or something.'

'Don't worry, Brian!' said Hugh. 'I've been ballooning for years. Joe knows his stuff. Have you got a woolly hat, Dan?'

'A woolly hat?' Before I could reply Joe turned into a private drive flanked on each side by an avenue of trees clearly visible now in the early dawn light.

'Oh dear,' said Brian, 'is this private land do you think?' Joe drove right up to the rear of a very large house. Brian pulled up behind and we gathered together in the gloom.

'What are you going to do, Joe?' said Brian, looking anxiously at the Range Rover and Porsche standing in the back yard. 'It looks pretty private . . .'

'I'm going to knock them up and ask if we can fly from the park over there – perfect it is. Perfect!'

'But it's four in the morning, Joe! You can't just . . .!' Too late. Joe marched up to the door. There was no bell, so he started banging on it loudly at regular intervals!

'Oh dear . . .' said Brian, and we shrank down behind the Range Rover. Eventually a light came on upstairs and a window opened. A figure appeared in a silk dressing gown and leant out.

'What do you want?' snapped the figure.

'Can I fly my balloon from your field, guv?' said Joe!

'Can you what!'

'Can I fly my balloon . . .' Joe started.

'It's four in the morning!' the figure said.

'Best time,' said Joe. This stumped the figure a bit.

'Well, couldn't you have rung last night?' it asked pretty reasonably in the circumstances.

'No,' said Joe, a man of few words. He didn't think it worth trying to explain to the figure the intricacies of balloon flying.

'Well, I think it's a BIT ORFF!' said the figure. 'You should have written or something.'

Brian sensed things were not going our way and he bobbed up from behind the Range Rover. 'Er, I say . . . We're from the BBC, you see . . .' Brian explained apologetically.

'Oh!' said the figure resignedly, 'I suppose that will be all right then.' And it disappeared.

Such is the power of Aunty Beeb! Anyhow, off we went into the park next to the house.

Joe's balloon was enormous – nearly eighty feet high by the time it was full of hot air, and it towered over the basket, straining to be off.

'Right,' said Joe, 'all aboard.' And in we got. The basket was large enough for seven or eight people, so with just Joe, Hugh, Brian and I there was bags of room.

'You'd better have this spare woolly hat,' said Hugh. 'It gets pretty hot when Joe lights the burners.' Joe lit up, and there was a roar of gas and flame just above our heads sending hot air up into the gaping mouth of the balloon. Joe shouted to his team to cast off, and up we went.

Some experiences in life are as clear in memory as the day they happened. The balloon ride was pure magic. It was a perfect May morning with a bright blue sky, and the air as clear and sparkly as you could imagine.

'I just hadn't realized,' I said to Hugh excitedly, 'there's no wind!' And of course, there wasn't. We proceeded gently at the same speed as what wind there was, and, apart from Joe's occasional lighting of the burner, we drifted, silent and dream-like, across the countryside. There was no feeling of fear looking down over the side of the basket – just pure wonder, as the Herefordshire landscape slid gently by.

Hugh and I chatted away whilst Brian happily recorded.

'You can certainly see the farming pattern from here,' I said.

'Yes,' said Hugh sadly. 'It's changed a lot in modern times, hasn't it?'

I grinned to myself. 'Well, Hugh, the main difference between today and fifty years ago would be colour. At that time, without fertilizer, there'd have been none of these super shades of green: dark blue-green wheat; jade green grass for silage; delicate light green barley. It really is beautiful . . .'

Hugh decided to change the subject. 'About coming down, Dan. Have you flown before?'

'No,' I said.

'Ah,' said Hugh. 'It can be a bit rough. Can't it, Joe?'

'Oh, yes,' said Joe happily, 'can be pretty exciting.'

'Oh!' I said. 'What do you mean?'

'Well,' said Hugh, making sure Brian was still recording, 'last trip we crashed into a hedge at twenty miles an hour. The basket turned over and the chap I was interviewing fell out!'

'Nasty that was,' agreed Joe, 'last thing you must do when we touch down is get out . . . lightens the balloon you see, and up we go again!'

I looked down at the dream-like scene passing slowly below and shook my head. 'It doesn't look bad from here.'

'Never does,' said Hugh triumphantly.

Brian decided he'd 'got enough'; 'Shall we go down, Joe?'

'Fine,' said Joe. 'Still only eight thirty, though.'

'We ought to get back to Bristol,' said Brian regretfully.

'OK,' said Joe, and down we went.

We landed like a piece of thistledown in the middle of a large grass field. Joe had radio contact with his ground crew who were on the way, and we stood chatting idly in the morning sunshine waiting for them to arrive.

A small boy appeared at the field gate, together with a woman – presumably his mother. The boy raced across the field to skid to a stop in front of the balloon.

'This is my dad's field,' he said breathlessly.

'Think he'll mind?' said Joe.

'No,' said the boy.

'Want a ride?' asked Joe.

The boy's eyes came out on organ stops. 'A ride!' he said incredulously.

'Yes,' said Joe. 'Hop in.' The small boy hopped in.

The ground crew arrived at the gate; two of them joined us.

'Do you mind if I give the crew a ride?' Joe asked Brian. Brian and I got out to balance the weight and Joe lit up; then he, the two ground crew, Hugh and the small boy lifted gently off into the beautiful spring morning.

'Will Johnny be all right?' asked his mother, looking a bit worried.

'I should think so,' I replied airily, still under the influence of

79

the balloon. Brian, the mother and I piled into the Land Rover with the remaining crew member and we set off in pursuit of the balloon. We were soon busy searching the map for a way to follow Joe's instructions over the radio.

'I'm going to have to come down,' Joe's voice said. 'Thermals are building up a bit!' Thermals! I was quite glad to be out of the basket. 'Sounds a bit dicey,' I said to the crew member.

'Don't worry about them,' said the crew member, 'Joe's just having a good time!'

'I'm over a wood,' said Joe, 'but I think we can come down in a clearing just off a track that comes from the road you're on.'

'Got you,' said the crew member, glancing down at the map as we drove along.

'Here we go,' said Joe. 'Ah – it's a bit steeper than I thought! – WATCH OUT . . .' With that communications were lost.

'What's happened?' said the mother.

'Sounds like a spot of bother!' said the crew member. 'Hold tight . .' and the Land Rover shot into a narrow track that wound through the woodland as we dashed along in fine style to the rescue. We found the balloon about a hundred yards from the track perched precariously on a near-vertical slope.

'All right, Joe?' shouted the crew member.

'Yes, but you're just in time!' Joe shouted back. Ropes were thrown and we all pulled; the balloon came off the slope.

'Let the air out!' ordered Joe. The crew member yanked a rope, a large flap opened in its top to let out the hot air, and with a large sigh the balloon settled down to earth.

'Well, that was a bit hairy,' said Joe, grinning widely.' I thought we might turn right over!'

'Did you enjoy it?' I asked the small boy as we stood watching the balloon being packed away into its basket.

'It was great,' he said breathlessly. 'I loved it!'

'So did I,' I said.

1976

1976 was the year of the worst drought in living memory for the south-west. I started off all right; the sheep had just begun to make some money and I was carrying 800 ewes on Netton plus 250 hill ewes on the cliff. To take advantage of the mild climate I used to 'double crop' as much land as I could. After the barley had been harvested we'd sow a catch crop of rape or turnips at the end of August. This would be used for fattening lambs and as winter feed for the ewes. This catch-cropping land – 150 acres or so – would be ploughed in March when the sheep had finished and then put into spring barley.

The 1976 winter had been exceptionally dry, particularly after Christmas. The biggest field on the farm was Stoke Field – forty-one acres – and we'd finished feeding off a crop of rape there by the third week in March.

'How's it going, Preston?' I asked.

'Fine, Boss. It's coming up so dry that you could sow the barley right away.'

I'd walked out from the farm to see how Preston was getting on with the plough. In Stoke Field he took nearly a quarter of an hour to go forward and back the full length of the field. I'd stood watching him coming towards me in the spring sunshine.

He was being followed by the usual crowd of gulls eager for the chance of a worm from the freshly turned earth.

'I see what you mean!' I answered, kicking the soil with my boot. It broke up into 'fine tilth', with no effort at all.

'I suppose that means we're in for a wet year to make up for no rain this winter?'

'Either that or it'll be blamed dry,' replied Preston. 'I don't think there's enough moisture to get the barley to germinate.'

'Well we'd better get on and drill it, then,' I said. 'If we get it in in the next couple of days it'll be ready for the rain when it does come.'

'Look. I'll come and plough for you at lunch time. Then I'll go on this afternoon with the other tractor and the harrows and start working down.'

The farm looked well that spring. The winter corn was dark green and lush and there was plenty of grass. We'd lambed earlier that year and each field had its complement of ewes and lambs all looking spry and happy. Better put some more nitrogen on the grass, I remember thinking that day. If it stays dry we'll need to get it growing well. We'd the best crops of lambs we'd had for years and they'd soon be eating a fair bit of grass as they became more independent of their mothers' milk.

We worked Stoke Field down in record time. There's an old saying about a peck of March dust being worth its weight in gold. But that year it was so dry the tractors were covered in it, and so were Preston and I. We finished sowing the barley on March 24th.

'Went well,' I said as we tidied up the empty sacks round the trailer.

'Yes, but it's blinking dry,' said Preston. 'I've never seen it as dry as this in March in forty years here. There's no sign of the wet place over there near the road. The spring must have dried up completely.'

At that time of the year the barley should have been up in ten days to a fortnight, but a month later, instead of lines of fresh green plants the field was a sorry sight. There was the odd plant here and there about every two or three yards, then you'd find half a dozen that had managed to find some moisture from somewhere. The rest of the soil was dead and barren. I could find the grains of barley when I dug for them, still inert and waiting for rain. The fertilizer we'd sown with the barley was also still there. It should have dissolved by now in the moist soil, but there it was, grey-white granules, easy to spot in the brown dust.

'Are we getting a bit short of grass, Boss?' asked John. 'The sheep are very restless.'

'We need some rain, John,' I said. 'We've actually cut the stock this year, but if it goes on like this we'll need to feed the ewes to keep them milking . . .'

'What about the cliff ewes? The grass is dying out there already.'

It was true. It wasn't the end of April and there were already large areas of brown showing up the thin soil over rock on the cliff ground.

'They're fine at the moment,' I said. 'They're nearly all singles and those hill ewes manage on pretty poor pasture anyway.' Although the main-flock ewes on the temporary pasture land started looking hungry and pinched, the cliff ewes were very content – well spread out and enjoying the fine dry weather.

By the middle of May the situation with the sheep had become desperate. Netton is a dry farm and without regular rain the thin soil simply runs out of moisture. The grassland had stopped growing and the sheep had eaten every field into the ground. We were feeding out full winter rations and most of the ewes spent the day waiting for John and the cake bag. They'd lost most of their milk and the lambs had suffered badly – not that we'd lost any, but instead of fat, chubby frames getting ready for market, they were more like greyhounds – perfectly fit but not enough meat on them to satisfy even a lapsed vegetarian.

Apart from Stoke Field the crops looked reasonably well; winter roots were well down, they'd found enough moisture. But we had wheat in ear on May 21st: unheard of. And whatever the weather did from now on, it looked like an early harvest. Stoke Field was a disaster – less than 5 per cent of the barley had germinated and the sparse clumps had been joined by the odd thistle – doing extremely well thanks to the lack of competition.

'We'll have to wean the ewes. That's all there is to it. The lambs aren't getting any milk and it will be a lot easier to feed them properly with the old girls out of the way.'

'Where will we put them?' asked John.

'I'll have to find some "keep" for them somewhere. Unless we can spread the lambs out they'll never get fat.'

This was the first in a string of wrong decisions I made that year. If only I'd decided to sell the ewes and cut my losses. I found a friend in Wiltshire who farmed a large acreage of the army training land on Salisbury Plain.

'I'll take them gladly, Dan. I'll have to charge you something: a shilling a head a week – will that be all right?'

It was a pretty low figure, although still adding £200 a month to the bills.

'That would be great, Richard,' I said. 'I'll come up to see how they've settled in a week or so.'

By the time I went up to see the ewes it was well into June and I was glad to get away from Netton. The whole farm was looking dry and parched now. The corn ripened early, and the so-called grassland fields were white – the only patches of green a couple of deeper wet spots on the cliff. I'd given up going to look at Stoke Field. Whatever problems the so-called crop might have, it wouldn't be worth treating. The winter corn on the heaviest land looked reasonable, but the rest of the farm was getting worse daily.

Salisbury Plain was a revelation, and Richard smiling a welcome as always.

'We'll have a cup of tea first, Dan, then I'll take you out to look at the sheep.'

'How have they settled in?' I asked.

'Fine,' he said, 'they have been no trouble at all, thank goodness, as I've just lost my shepherd.'

'Lost your shepherd?'

'Well I didn't actually lose him,' laughed Richard. 'It was mutual. I had a job finding the right chap and in the end took on this man who'd been a shepherd in the Falklands. His best reference was one that said he was a real champion at driving sheep through water. Apparently they drive sheep through shallow sea crossings to get at island grazing.'

'There's not a lot of water on Salisbury Plain,' I said.

'None at all on this bit,' Richard agreed cheerfully, 'and unfortunately it was all my shepherd did know about sheep, so I had to let him go.'

After a cup of tea we set off in Richard's little Renault van, bouncing across the tank tracks to see the ewes. They were happy as sandboys penned in a large area by an electric fence, green grass to eat and no responsibilities whatsoever.

'They're great, Richard,' I said. 'They've put on weight since you've had them. Look, can I leave them with you until September?'

'That'll be fine, Dan. Now whilst you're here you mentioned you might need a bit of hay?'

Need a bit of *hay*! I could have taken Richard's arm off at the elbow!

'We make a couple of hundred tonnes a year to sell off this land,' explained Richard. 'We can't farm it properly as it's used by the tanks. If you grow a decent crop they come and try and hide in it.'

As Richard explained the vagaries of army land he showed me his first-class hay, and I bought enough to see Netton through the next winter whatever the weather. I paid up for the hay and sheep 'keep' so far and left to return to Devon – poorer but happier than I'd been in months.

Back at Netton we had 1,400 lambs that were living on dry feed. Life without green grass and Mum was definitely not for them, and whilst they were all fit and well they refused to get fat. They were costing well over £200 a week to feed, but what else could we do? If only I'd sold them! But then it had to rain sometime, surely . . .

By the time the children broke up for summer holidays in July we were well into harvest. It was three weeks early and whilst my family spent day after glorious day on the beach I got more and more depressed as the pitifully small heaps of grain in the corn store refused to grow. In the end I could put off the evil day no longer and we harvested the 41 acres of Stoke Field. Normally I would have expected 80 tonnes; 60 would have been a poor crop. We cut just three trailer loads – 16 tonnes. The final insult was that the grain was so light and pinched that we had to empty the combine into the trailers beside the road hedge to stop the shrivelled grains blowing away across the field.

At this time I gave up hoping for rain and I decided to sell the lambs. I found a buyer from the middle of the county. On his heavy land the weather had been perfect and he had grass coming out of his ears – not that it stopped him driving a hard bargain. We picked out 972 lambs, and after considerable haggling and arm twisting, came to a price of £12 each. It was all I could expect, although it meant a big loss when compared with what they would have made as fat lambs. The worst part was that they would have made nearly as much in May, several thousand pounds earlier! Anyway the price was agreed. 'Nine hundred and seventy-two at twelve pounds – that'll be twelve thousand, seven hundred and sixty four pounds,' I said.

'We'll make it the round twelve thousand seven hundred,' said the buyer, making out the cheque.

'Hang on,' I said, 'we agreed twelve pounds a head. And I wasn't too happy about that! You can't just knock off sixty-four pounds.'

'Well then,' he said, closing his cheque book, 'if you're not happy I'd just as soon leave it.'

I had to swallow my pride . . . I had to sell!

'All right,' I said, 'twelve thousand seven hundred it is.'

Once the harvest was over I opened all the gates, and what was left of the lambs plus the hill flock from the cliff roamed over the whole farm, picking over the stubble, eating hedges – anything. By the end of August you could have chased a mouse from one end of the farm to the other without ever losing sight of it – there was *nothing* left. But the worst blow of all was that the grass had died. Normally perennial grasses, although they do go brown in dry weather, recover when it rains, sending new green shoots from what looks like a parched dead plant. But always, if you look closely, you'll find the succulent signs of life right at the base of the old dry stems.

'It's dead, all right.' My friend Don was an expert on grasses. We'd been digging up grass plants on the bare pasture fields for over an hour.

'Look. The roots are just fibrous and dry, there's not a sign of life. I'm afraid you'll have to re-seed the lot!'

'Whew!' I said, 'that's a hundred and forty acres! By the time we've ploughed and worked it down it'll cost over twenty pounds an acre.' Nearly £3,000 that I couldn't afford.

'You've no choice,' said Don bluntly. 'And I think you're better off than some chaps I've been to see. At least we can see yours is dead, in a lot of cases on heavier land it's a matter of wait and see, and I'm afraid that if they make the wrong decision they'll have no grass next year.'

We took Don's advice and ploughed everything – re-seeding all the grassland. Then, at last, after six months of unrelenting drought, it rained. I can remember standing outside the back door and just letting it soak me to the skin – wonderful! By the end of September Netton was green again. The ewes had returned from their holiday in Wiltshire, fresh and keen to meet the rams again, and the remainder of the lambs were fattening quickly on fresh new pastures.

The final insult of the year came from Stoke Field, however.

'Well, look at that, Boss! Dashed barley's germinated after all!' Preston and I were looking over the fence from the field next door, and there, sure enough, amongst the sparse stubble of the crop we'd harvested you could see a healthy crop of barley coming up in perfect rows – six months, almost to the week, after sowing.

'Pity it's spring barley, Boss. Do you want me to plough it up?' And that was the final ignominy. I had to agree; yes, Preston should plough it. It was pointless to leave the spring crop that would simply be killed off by the winter's frost.

By the end of October the farm was back to normal. We'd brought the first load of hay down from Wiltshire and settled in for the winter, and I counted up the cost. In extra expense and lost yields, 1976 had cost £25,000 – another year like it would have finished me.

HORSES

I've never been keen on horses. As far as I'm concerned they're dangerous, unreliable and an expensive way of doing anything on a farm. Give me a tractor or motorbike any day. My family never agreed with that, and as soon as the girls were old enough to wield a riding crop, my wife, Sandy, persuaded me that we must have a horse 'for the children'. Well, persuaded is not quite the right word; I agreed, though, as long as looking after the animal was nothing to do with me.

'We'll get a Shetland.' I was careful not to hear too much of the excited planning. Jane was worried it wouldn't be big enough for her, but Bindy, my second daughter, rounded on Jane and said a Shetland would be great. She'd been studying Thelwell and knew what perfect 'starter' ponies they were! All I could remember about the breed was that they could be a bit crabby at times, but I knew better than to offer my two pennyworth.

I was right, of course, the Shetland was not just a 'bit crabby', it turned out to be the Devil Incarnate. It simply hated being ridden, preferring to stay in its field, getting fatter and fatter. Whenever the girls set out to catch it there would be a prolonged battle with the pony flying round and round the two-acre field like some sort of demented spider – short black legs stretched out from its little fat body.

'I've been bitten!' Bindy, chubby cheeks stained with angry tears, announced; she turned round and dropped her jodhpurs. 'Look, it hurts!' On her plump white behind, the Shetland had left a perfect set of teeth marks.

'It's no good, the pony will have to go,' Sandy said, trying not to smile. I solemnly agreed, but when I suggested sending it to market I was firmly shouted down.

'We couldn't do that. He must go to a good home.' I started to point out that the 'he' was an 'it', but was firmly put in my place.

'Mr H. will look after him. He'll find a nice farm.' Mr H. was a horse dealer in the village and the Shetland duly departed, to be replaced by Topsy, a four-year-old mare.

I met Mr H. at market a couple of weeks later. We greeted each other and chatted about the weather and such for a few minutes.

'I'm impressed that you managed to find a good home for the Shetland, Horace,' I said. 'It really was a bad tempered pony.'

Mr H. looked at me quietly for a minute then he said contemplatively. 'A good home . . . ah, yes, sir, he'll be fine as long as he doesn't get sea-sick.'

Poor old Shetland. At that time the only boat trip for ponies was across to the horse butchers in France.

Topsy was everything the Shetland hadn't been: quiet, with endless patience, and she was tormented in turn, by all four of my children. As their interest began to wane I wondered if we should find a good home for Topsy – perhaps Mr H.? Sandy was very firm, 'Get rid of Topsy? She's part of the family. No. I thought we might let her rear a foal!'

Well, one horse on a farm is a nuisance; two can be ten times worse. I knew that, what with separate fields and getting too fat. But I also knew that argument was pointless. All I'd get would be a steady look and a reminder that the farm was our home as well as a business. The final argument which made me agree with alacrity was that 'it won't cost as much as your fishing.'

I missed the nuptials, but by all accounts it was quite an event. Sandy had called on two New Zealanders who were working on the farm to help. The stallion was called Winston Lad, or something, and was well over twenty years old.

'Poor old b . . . was on his last legs, Boss,' one of the New Zealanders told me. 'Took him nearly an hour to get his dander up and then we had to get one on each leg and hoist him aboard.' It really was a case of grandfather's last stand too. Winston had gone into decline and died quietly just two weeks afterwards. Splash arrived in the late spring, after days of worry and agonizing by Sandy and the girls. Topsy took matters in hand and there he was, all legs, and with an impossibly short body, standing unsteadily in the morning sunshine. He was christened Splash. I'm not quite sure why, but somehow it seemed to suit him. I say 'him', but of course he wasn't allowed to stay a 'him' for long.

In due course we had two horses for anyone who cared to ride. The only drawback was that you couldn't take Topsy out on her own – Splash had to come too; he got really worked up if they were separated. And as the children began to leave home it became quite a worry. Topsy, of course, was part of the furniture and was expected to stay for ever. Splash was another matter. He was a lively pony and obviously capable of better things. But how could we separate him from his mother?

Nature has a way of taking care of those things, and Topsy was well into her teens when she quite suddenly fell ill and died. She spent her last few hours in an old barn with Splash. Sandy called me up late in the evening, and poor old Topsy was lying in the straw, obviously in pain. I knelt beside the horse to give Sandy a rest from her long vigil, and the quiet brown eyes looked at me sadly. Splash was standing quietly a few feet away when Topsy whinnied urgently. Splash replied, and for a few minutes you could feel the communication flowing between mother and son. When I say feel, I mean just that. The rapport between the two was so strong that it literally charged the small stone barn, dark except for the light from our torches. Then Topsy relaxed, and with a quivering gusty sigh, the gentle lady died.

We left Splash on his own with his mother that night, and in the morning he simply walked out of the barn and followed Sandy down to his paddock. He never fretted or pined. He just seemed to have grown up. But keeping him on his own was not possible, so he was sent to a neighbour whose daughter was keen on 'bringing horses on'.

Sandy was right and he made the grade too. He's now the prized possession of a dedicated pony-clubber, meeting the challenge of all and sundry every weekend in the season.

I don't suppose I'd know him if I saw him again, but Topsy . . . well, she was something special.

HAY, STRAW AND FIRE

To be a 'proper farmer' means being philosophical to the point that drives one to distraction. Either that, or it turns you into an abject pessimist. The old joke about a farmer and his neighbour standing looking over the gate tells it all. They're looking at the farmyard full to bursting with hayricks and cornricks – a real bumper year without doubt.

'Well, Joe, best harvest you've ever had,' says the neighbour.

'Maybe,' says the farmer gloomily, 'but what'll I do if I have a fire?' This miserable outlook comes from fighting a losing battle with Nature. Mine started the first year I was at Netton.

Cattle and sheep were expensive to buy and instead of stocking the farm to the hilt, Father advised me to make some hay. 'You've plenty of room in the Dutch barn, Dan,' he said, 'and hay keeps. Having a good reserve of hay is the best insurance against a hard winter.' I was gripped with enthusiasm . . . reserves of fodder!

'Right,' I said, 'I'll cut Well Park Field and Shannon's Down – that'll be forty acres. How many bales to the acre do you think I'll get?'

Father smiled. 'You've got to get it first!' he said. 'Forty acres is quite a bit. You should get between two and three thousand bales.'

I quickly learnt that making hay in the average English summer is regarded as an art rather than a science. The first decision you have to take is when to cut it: if you cut it early whilst the grass is green and sappy, it makes top quality hay, but it takes a long time to 'make'. Making is letting the sun dry out the crop until it's safe to bale it up and put it in the barn. Bale it too quick and it heats up. Not that a little heat hurts. In fact you need a bit to 'make' the hay properly. But if you bale it too green, it can get very hot indeed – so hot that you get spontaneous combustion!

If you wait until the grass has gone to seed the hay makes faster all right, but it's lost most of its goodness for sheep and is only fit for older cattle or horses. Once you've cut the stuff, you're committed. It takes about a week to get hay fit for the baler in early June, and the last thing you want then is rain. My neighbour, David, explained all this to me when I went to him for advice.

'Oh, and when you've cut it with the mower, Dan, don't turn it unless you're sure the weather's going to be dry. If you turn it and *then* it rains, you'll spoil it for sure.'

'When should I cut it, then?' I asked. 'It looks about ready to me.'

'I'd wait for the new moon two weeks next Friday,' said David.

Wait for the new moon! 'What on earth for?' I asked.

'That's the way we do it,' shrugged David.

I went back to the hay fields. It was a beautiful June day, the crop was thick and lush . . . wait for two weeks on Friday! I went down to the farm and rang the weather man. 'Chance of showers over the next couple of days. Atlantic low. Fine by the weekend!'

I went out to consult Preston. 'Well,' he said, 'might be better to leave it a bit.'

'But the crop's perfect, Preston. It'll go to seed by the end of next week. Look, why don't we cut it now? We can wait and turn it after the Atlantic low's gone!'

'You're the boss,' said Preston happily. 'I'll hitch up the mower.'

The next day we'd cut one field and I decided we'd carry on and cut the whole forty acres. The weatherman was still predicting fine weather after a couple of showery days. The hay looked perfect. On Friday evening the sky cleared. We'd only had a couple of light showers, not enough to penetrate the heavy swathes of hay lying on the ground.

'We'll turn it tomorrow if it's fine,' I said to Preston.

I'd asked David who'd suggested I'd cut it a bit too soon and I ought to wait several days before turning it. That was too chancy I decided – much better get on with the job.

'Don't think we ought to leave it till Monday?' asked Preston.

'Not if it's fine, Preston,' I said. 'We've got to get on, you know.'

Saturday was fine . . . beautiful, in fact – blazing sun, drying breeze. The hay fluffed up by the turner was drying out a perfect emerald green! If we got it right I'd have the best hay in the parish. It would only take a couple more days. Sunday was dull and grey. The hay looked limp and lifeless – all yesterday's crackle gone out of it.

I rang the weatherman. 'New Atlantic low. Heavy rain expected within twenty-four hours!'

'What!' I said. 'But it can't be. You said it was going to be fine! Are you there . . .? are you there . . .?' The weatherman had rung off.

It rained for most of Monday. It was dry Tuesday and Wednesday. We turned the hay again, white and bleached now . . . second quality at best. It rained from Friday till Monday . . . we turned it again. It rained again.

''Tis ruined!' said Preston. 'Look, it's gone black . . . cut too green! 'Tisn't worth baling!'

By now it was Friday fortnight and the new moon had come. David had started cutting his hay . . . a bit seedy, but it would make quickly! I looked at the blackened sodden swathes . . . fresh green grass trying to poke up through them from the sward below.

'We'll have to get rid of it, Preston. It'll kill the new grass otherwise.'

'Quickest way'll be to turn it and bale it!' Preston said, and that's what we did – turned it, baled it in clouds of black fungal spores, hauled it to the side of the field and then burnt it! All forty acres' worth! To this day I hate making the decision when to cut or turn hay, and, depending on which part of the country you're in, you'll find there's always a local traditional day to start – Cornwall Show day; a new moon; or, coming bang up to date, Wimbledon fortnight. There's no logic as far as I can see behind any of it, but it takes the agonizing decision away from the individual and you can then accept what God disposes with resignation.

Straw is much easier than hay because it starts off dry. As Netton was mostly arable there was always more straw than we needed, so when we'd got in enough for the winter I'd try to sell the rest. Selling straw is not the easiest job because it's a low value by-product (the grain of wheat and barley is what you grow the crops for, after all) so this means that the 'straw trade' attracts a fair few cowboys.

I got caught by Mr X the first harvest I was at Netton. I call him Mr X not because I'm worried by the laws of libel or slander, whichever it is, but because I've forgotten his name anyway. Mr X was an out-and-out crook.

'I run a very considerable business, Mr Cherrington,' Mr X told me. 'Here's my card!'

We had done a fine deal – thirty shillings an acre for fifty acres of straw – well over the market, and I kicked myself for having sold the lion's share to a local farmer for only twenty-five shillings. It just showed how you can be duped by a cunning neighbour – he'd said twenty-five shillings was the going rate.

Mr X's card was finely engraved: office premises, 4B Drake's

Circus, Plymouth. An office in the local town, no less.

'What about payment?' I asked.

'A cheque as soon as we clear the straw,' said Mr X, 'I'm sending in several lorries. If you can help them load we'll be gone by Friday.'

'Right,' I said, pocketing Mr X's card.

A motley assortment of lorries turned up. I was a bit surprised that Mr X didn't use a better looking fleet.

'Sub-contract,' Mr X explained airily as he wrote out the cheque.

'Seventy-five pounds. There we are . . . it's a pleasure to do business with you, Mr Cherrington.'

'Don't you want a receipt?' I asked.

'Oh, no,' said Mr X. 'You're a man of your word, Mr Cherrington . . . and anyway, I've got the straw, haven't I?'

Indeed he had. Later on, the following week, the bank rang up.

'Mr Cherrington?'

'Yes,' I said.

'We had a cheque for seventy-five pounds returned for insufficient funds, made out by Mr X.'

'Insufficient funds? What do you mean?' I asked with a sinking feeling in my stomach.

'It's bounced, Mr Cherrington . . .' said the bank clerk.

I went to Plymouth right away and asked directions. 'Drake's Circus? It's over there . . . See . . . empty it is! They're pulling it down for a new car park. Been empty for a couple of months!'

I walked disconsolately round and round 4B – black staring holes for windows. Empty. At £75 it was a sharp lesson!

Mind you, I was better off than Father. He got caught by a Cornishman who'd come up to Hampshire looking for straw one particularly dry summer. Father had had a fine deal – you couldn't give straw away in Hampshire, but it was scarce as hen's teeth in Cornwall. They decided the fairest way was to set a price depending on how many bales of straw the Cornishman got to the acre. The Cornishman was very enthusiastic and brought his baler and an old Fordson tractor to bale up the straw. He baled up thousands of bales and then it started raining. Father insisted the straw had to be shifted. The Cornishman said he couldn't sell wet straw. Father said that wasn't his problem, and what about the money he owed let alone clearing up thousands of bales of wet soggy straw? The Cornishman did a moonlight flit, but he hadn't been able to fit all his gear on the lorry, so he left his baler behind (no doubt reckoning to pick it up on a return load). But Father was too quick for him and he padlocked the baler to a sturdy oak tree with a heavy-duty chain!

For several months, nothing happened. We got rid of the soggy bales into an old chalk quarry, and the baler sat under the oak tree, waiting for its owner to face the music with Father. It must have been near Christmas when John Toms – my father's foreman – drove into the farmyard to find my father.

'Baler's gone, Boss!' he said.

'Baler?' said Father.

'Yes, you know, the one that there Cornish fellow left!'

'How on earth?' said Father. 'What did he do, pick the padlock?'

'No,' said John Toms. 'He came back with a chainsaw and cut down the oak tree!'

After my first harvest, unless I was sure I was going to get the money, I used to burn the surplus straw, and burning the straw (using a Bryant and May baler, we used to say) was very quick indeed. It left bare black fields if you got it right, clean and ready for the autumn cultivations.

I know straw-burning is a dirty word today, and the practice is shortly to become illegal. Quite rightly so. Anyone who's been in the eastern counties of England in late August will have experienced the smoke and ashes, with daylight blocked out as the whole countryside is covered by a thick pall of smoke, the roar and crackle of dozens of fires making an unnatural glow on the skyline, so that it's like being in a scene from Dante's

Inferno. Netton was never quite like that, but it was a pretty hairy practice.

One of the arguments against straw-burning is that it's a bit tough on the wildlife – insects and field mice that get caught up in the conflagration. I agree that this cremation sounds horrible, but I wonder how many people watching seagulls following the plough think of what's actually going on. For anything too slow to get out of the way the choice is to be buried alive or gobbled up by the gulls.

Anyway, I burnt straw with the same enthusiasm that I tackled anything. The advice was to let the straw burn slowly and steadily against the wind. In that way the fire wouldn't get out of hand. The trouble was, if you did that, it seldom burnt completely and you'd be left with annoying patches of unburnt stubble that were more difficult to cultivate. If you lit it with the wind you were much more likely to get a clean burn, but the fire then took over, particularly if the wind was strong! The first time I decided to try for a clean burn was in Tank Field. Tank Field, so called because of a tank that used to be in it, is oblong with a track at the eastern end which makes a natural fire-break. I wanted to seed the field out to grass as quickly as possible after harvest, to get some nice fresh autumn grazing for the stock. If I got a clean burn, it meant I didn't have to plough the field – just a quick cultivation and on with the job. John was on hand with his tractor and the crop sprayer filled with water mounted on the back.

'John, you stay out in that grass field,' I said. 'You'll be able to see what goes on, and if the hedge should catch on fire you can come in and we'll have some water to put it out. I'll light things up with the Fordson.'

'Righto, Dan,' said John cheerfully, and he got into his tractor and drove out of the gate into the field next door.

The Fordson was a reliable old workhorse without a cab, which made it easy to hop on and off (this was long before farm safety and anti-roll bars). I'd made a firelighter out of old sacks soaked in diesel oil, plus an old tyre. The bundle was attached to the Fordson's tow bar by a long chain, and it lay on a patch of bare earth inside Tank Field's gate. I adjusted the sacks and tyre for the umpteenth time and tested the westerly breeze with my finger. It was getting stronger, no doubt of that. It had been dry for several days and we were in for a belt of rain moving in from the Atlantic. If the straw got wet it would take days to dry again, and we'd have to 'turn it' with the hay turner. It was definitely now or never. To hell with it, I thought, the fire couldn't do any damage however strongly the wind made it burn. All the surrounding fields were bare grassland.

It took several matches to get the firelighter to catch. The strong breeze kept blowing the matches out, but in the end it caught, and, fuelled by the diesel, started burning persistently, giving off a small trail of thick black smoke. I hopped onto the Fordson. I'd decided to drive round Tank Field in a big U, starting and finishing at the track at its eastern end. In that way I reckoned the fire should burn the whole field cleanly. We'd baled the outside round of straw and cultivated the stubble, so the fire should keep out of the hedges, and the track where I was starting would act as a fire break and put the fire out. Nothing could go wrong, could it, I thought. And taking a deep breath I set off slowly up the southern boundary of the field.

The firelighter bounced and bumbled along ten yards or so behind me at the end of the chain. Too fast, I thought, the fire's not catching. Then I saw odd small delicate patches of flame rising in my wake. It was catching after all. It was just taking its time to get going. Fine, I thought. Just right. It must have taken ten minutes or so for me to reach the far end of the field. The Fordson was chugging along steadily. I could see the fire was established along the whole of the southern boundary and was burning well, gradually moving out into the field, burning across the stiffening westerly breeze. I'd better step on it a bit, I thought. The fire would probably go a bit faster when I lit it with the wind. Then the thought crossed my mind that I was at the furthest point from the nearest escape route from the field, the road gate at the north-east corner. Too late to worry now. I put the Fordson in top gear and set off across the western boundary – a Devon bank topped by a stunted thorn hedge. It only took a couple of minutes to reach the next corner of the field, and as I turned to head for the road gate I glanced back the way I'd come.

At the far side of the field the fire had taken hold with a vengeance. The crop wasn't heavy and the flames were devouring stubble and straw with consummate ease fanned by the westerly wind. I decided not to hang about but set off down the northern boundary. I hadn't gone more than two hundred yards, with four hundred still to go, when I heard the threatening roar behind me. Looking back there was a wall of flame racing down the full width of the field – flames in sheets were sweeping forward, lighting up the field in ten- to twenty-yard gulps. Due to the wind the fire was burning almost horizontally – I'll never make it, I thought! I had to decide whether to abandon ship, leaving the Fordson to its fate and try to get over the steep Devon hedge with its thick topping of thorns or . . .

Looking back, that's what I should have done, but in moments like that you don't think, you just act. I turned the Fordson to face the flames, and then opening the throttle simply drove straight back towards the racing fire as fast as she'd go, putting my jacket up over my head as I went. I must have been through the flames in less than half a second. The combined opposing speeds of the Fordson and the fire were probably around forty miles per hour. There was a brief moment of intense heat, but I was too busy trying to control the Fordson as it bumped and jolted across the rough field. I stopped, and pulled my jacket back down. The fire had gone! It must have covered the length of Tank Field, a good six hundred yards, in less than five minutes. All that was left were a few spindly columns of smoke streaming across the blackened earth – it had burnt as clean as a whistle!

I got shakily off the tractor and leant against the wheel and waited as John appeared on his tractor, driving up across the burnt stubble.

'You all right?' John asked, as he came up grinning. 'Went pretty quick, didn't it!'

The other time I experienced the power and ferocity of fire at Netton was when the cliff land went up. Funnily enough it wasn't in the very dry year of 1976 – the sheep had eaten every blade of grass out there that year and there was literally nothing left to burn – it was several years later, when the gorse had come back with a vengeance to defeat my efforts over twenty years to get rid of it for ever.

We'd had a dry July and August and the harvest had been the easiest for years. We hadn't quite finished in fact, and I was busy that particular Sunday morning, as I'd decided to make a start on a late field of beans. I'd picked up the combine from the last corn field where it had been left, at the western end of the farm, and was driving it eastward through the fields along the top of the cliff. It was hot and dry as a bone with an arid east wind, and I'd got about a third of the way along when I noticed a small plume of smoke at the edge of the gorse below the fence. I was driving across a ploughed field, and so it was quite safe to leave the combine where it was, and I ran across to investigate. Whilst there was no risk to the cultivated land now that harvest was over, the cliff was tinder dry and the flock of Swaledale ewes were picking away at the dried grass and whatever green shoots they could find on the block of cliff grazing at this end. I reached the fence. There was fire in a patch of rough grass just above the gorse. It couldn't have been going for long. The flames were crackling and moving from clump to clump amongst the grass like a living thing, going slowly westward along the top of the cliff. I suppose the area that had been burnt was no more than half an acre or so. I'd taken a sack with me from the combine and I jumped over the fence. If I could stop it reaching the gorse it would burn itself out against the field fence.

Whilst the fire was well established, it wasn't that hot, and I ran through the small dancing flames to get ahead of it. Then I turned to attack it with my sack. *Whoomph* – the centre of the patch of flame I hit was put out but the outsides were still going . . . *Whoomph* . . . *Whoomph* . . . I was gradually winning. The fire was pushing me back certainly, but the front I was fighting was being pushed towards the fence. If only John, who had been waiting with the tractor and trailer in the bean field, would realize something was wrong and come looking for me, together we'd have it under control in no time . . . As if in answer to my prayers I heard John's tractor coming roaring along the edge of the ploughed field. I looked up, panting, literally drenched with sweat, as he got out of the tractor cab and ran up to the fence.

'Dan! You'd better come quick. The whole cliff's on fire the other side of the coast guard lookout!' John was white as a sheet.

'Right,' I said. 'Go back to the farm and call the fire brigade. I'll stay out here and see what I can do. Bring a couple of flat shovels back to help beat the flames. Go . . . quick!'

John turned and ran back to his tractor. I went back to the flames. Hell, I thought, what about the sheep? John had said the whole slope was on fire! I set about the flames grimly. If I let it get hold here that would be both ends of this section of cliff land on fire – any sheep in the middle would stand a good chance of being in a barbecue!

Crackle . . . whoosh! I glanced back eastward. A clump of grass I thought I'd put out had got going again, and the worst had happened. The fire had got into the gorse. The gorse that year had flowered all spring and summer – beautiful yellow flowers for weeks on end, so that now the blooms had died down the bushes were laden with fat gorse seeds full of oil. The result was that when a bush caught fire it went up like a bonfire soaked with petrol, and if the bushes touched to form a solid clump, then the whole lot went up with spectacular ferocity.

The line of gorse that spread down over the cliff was alight over a twenty-yard face within less than a minute and there was no hope whatsoever of stopping it. The heat was so intense you had to shield your face from it a good thirty to forty feet away. With a sickening feeling I climbed back over the fence. I'd have to leave it to the fire brigade. Either they'd manage to stop it before it reached my neighbour David's cliff land or it would burn right to the headland two miles away. A large cove cut into the cliff between David's land and mine and there was only a thin strip of gorse there . . . perhaps, if they were quick enough . . .

It was no use worrying about that. John would raise the alarm, so I turned and ran back along the top of the cliff towards the look-out station. The look-out is on the highest point for miles and I couldn't see the cliff beyond it until I got there, although I could hear a sullen roar from the fire and I could see rolling clouds of dense smoke billowing across the cliff land as it stretched down to the sea to my right.

When I did reach the look-out I realized why John had looked a bit shaky. The fire had actually started in this part of the cliff. My bit had been an off-shoot that had raced along the dry grass at the foot of the fence that divided the cultivated fields from the cliff land. It had only managed to get back to the gorse where I'd left it a quarter of a mile away. Here the fire was firmly in command. The gorse was virtually solid and the fire was burning down across the cliff towards the rocks and the sea along a face a couple of hundred yards long – great tongues of flame and sparks were shooting into the air and the fire devoured new clumps of gorse as quickly as it could find enough oxygen to do so. The whole conflagration was moving inexorably westward and downward, driven by the east wind. The eastern end was still blazing but much less fiercely as the fire 'back burnt' into the breeze.

I couldn't see any sheep. The view to the bottom of the cliff was obscured by the thick black smoke, but there was nothing I could do anyway. Whatever sheep were there would have to take pot luck, I thought grimly. I decided to tackle the fire at its eastern end – at least there the wind would be helping, and it would keep me from worrying about the ewes until the fire brigade arrived – if they ever did. In fact, the fire brigade arrived almost as soon as I reached the eastern end of the fire.

Four or five of them appeared out of nowhere.

'Thank heavens you're here,' I said, as one offered me a spare flail to fight the flames.

'There's five engines the other end,' said the fireman cheerfully, 'over thirty of us.'

'I'm worried about the sheep,' I said, 'any that are trapped at the bottom of the gorse above the sheer cliffs proper . . . there are several flat areas they graze down there . . .'

'Right,' said the fireman briskly, 'I'll go back and tell the Chief. You carry on here if you like.'

Thankfully I resigned responsibility to the experts and turned to the sheer drudgery of beating out the fire. Even with expert help and guidance it must have taken us well over an hour to beat out the flames over the 150 yards from top to bottom of the cliff land. It wasn't as simple as simply bashing out the flames – it was so dry the fire 'splashed' as you hit it and the gorse bushes were just as likely to suddenly burst into flame again as the wind fanned a reluctant spark.

At the western end the fire brigade had arrived in the nick of time, but it had taken all their resources from the five engines to stop the fire getting into David's cliff. Then the men had fought the blaze all along the bottom edge of the gorse area where the sheep were trapped. They did a wonderful job and spared no effort to save the sheep. More than a hundred had been cut off by the fire in fact, but the only casualty was an old ewe with scorched feet who recovered completely in due course.

In the end we stopped it, but the fire had been so fierce, and the cliff so dry, that in large areas it had literally burnt the turf as well as the plants on top. Writing this, sitting at my desk in the middle of winter, I can still remember how completely helpless I felt that day, and the absolute power of the fire once it had taken hold.

FOXES

Coming from Hampshire, I wasn't used to foxes; Hampshire is shooting country and foxes were always very firmly controlled. Devon was different. The majority of farmers have an interest in hunting whether they ride or not, and it's a fact that wherever hunting is popular there are plenty of foxes. Most foxes don't eat lambs – they're happy to clean up natural deaths and after-births, but the odd one, usually a vixen feeding cubs, will take to killing and they can be a real pest. I lost half a dozen lambs to foxes the first year at Netton and there were always plenty about so we were perpetually at war – well, more like a series of running skirmishes.

My neighbour David warned me the cliff was a natural harbour for a fair number of foxes.

'How can I get at them out there?' I asked. 'It's as thick as blazes – no normal dog could get at them!'

'Try Phil,' said David, 'he's got a pack of Jack Russells.'

'We use guns, Dan,' said Phil, 'enough to surround a fair old acreage of gorse and brambles. Then we put the dogs in and stand quietly. The dogs are too slow to catch a fox but they stir them up and chase them out of the thickest undergrowth. Then, as they run out, a quick shot and it's all over . . .'

The shoot was arranged for a Saturday morning in November. My elder brother Syd had come down to see how I was getting on on the farm and was most intrigued to come along. Syd was a fine shot and got his sport on properly organized pheasant shoots in Hampshire. His enthusiasm tailed off a bit when he saw the guns arriving.

The first lot got out of a very ancient Transit van and stood around admiring each other's weapons and eagerly anticipating the sport. Syd watched them with alarm.

'Heavens, Dan, that chap's gun is held together with copper wire! And that one's got a pump gun! And look! That chap's loading up!'

I went over to persuade the enthusiast that he should keep his cartridges in his pocket until we'd left the farmyard.

'All right,' he said, 'but you never know when you're going to spot a fox with Phil's dogs around!' He swept a keen eye around the ground and buildings ready to go into action at the first sign of trouble.

'Look, Dan,' Syd came up looking a bit grim, 'I'm not too sure about this. One of those chaps has a sawn-off rifle. If he lets fly he could kill anything within half a mile. And . . .' he said, 'one or two are well away on whisky already.'

'Phil says they're all OK, Syd,' I tried to reassure him. 'They've been at this job for years and they've dealt with dozens of foxes.'

'Fine, but how many of them have got shot?'

I was beginning to think Syd had a point when Phil rolled up with the dogs in his large truck. He hopped out and came over for a council of war.

'Morning, Dan. Great morning for the job! We'll start at the east end of the cliff and drive it right through. Why don't you and your brother keep well ahead to deal with any foxes that run out? This lot'll stay with me.' With that Phil turned and started organizing the troups. 'Come on then, up this way. And don't load up yet. Wait till we clear the road.' Syd looked at me silently and then grinned and shook his head.

'At least we'll be out of range of the rifle! Can we find a place where we can watch in safety?'

I took Syd out to the coast guard lookout perched on the cliff top with grand all-round views. We watched Phil and his merry men go into action a mile or so away along the cliff. After a good deal of arguing and gesticulating the guns sorted themselves out. Several of the fitter ones forced their way down the slope to the bottom of the patch of gorse and brambles so that the area was loosely surrounded. The majority, however, moved along the track that wound along near the top of the cliff in a tight-knit group following the noise of the Jack Russells which had disappeared into the undergrowth. Everyone was ready to let fly at a fox. And I must say Syd and I were glad we were well out of range.

The little dogs were great. You'd see one appear from time to time out of the bushes, lost for a moment or two from its mates. It would shake itself and then listen, panting joyfully, to get its bearings again. As soon as it heard the general commotion of the rest of the pack it would yelp keenly, to plunge in again.

Three hours later the 'drive' had covered just over half the cliff land without seeing a thing. Phil called his dogs out of the bushes. Syd and I went down to see what was going on. We all stood round on a rocky headland, an open area with windswept turf and a few isolated gorse bushes. The dogs stood and lay around panting, quite happy to rest for a bit before going back to the fun. There must have been thirty or more guns standing around in an area the size of an average garden.

'There's no foxes out here, Master Phil,' a villainous looking hunter said who held his Damascus barrelled hammer-lock twelve bore cocked and ready, pointing skyward over his shoulder. Phil turned to me.

'I can't understand it, Dan! We've not even had the smell of a fox. These chaps are getting pretty fed up and one or two have gone home already.'

I was disappointed. 'I'm sure they're out here, Phil. We lost four lambs in the field just over the fence.'

'Fox'll travel miles to hunt,' one expert opined. 'Stands to reason they wouldn't live out here. The gorse is too blessed thick!' he added morosely, idly taking gorse prickles from the seat of his trousers.

'I vote we give up and go down to the pub,' said another. 'This is a waste of time and I could drink a gallon of beer.' The group began arguing amongst themselves, and it was clear that Phil was going to lose control. He looked across at me and shrugged.

'We'd better call it a day, Dan. Sorry. There's not much point in going on if half these chaps buzz off!' He turned to his dogs. 'Up boys! Come up, then.' Phil's calls roused the little terriers, who began to cast around, eager for action, and not realizing this was the end of the fun. One, keen to get started, stuck his nose in a small clump of gorse next to the rocky outcrop we were standing on and . . . out came a fox! Before you could say Jack Robinson it had dashed away along the track thirty yards or so to head straight down the cliff into one of the very steep gulleys that went right down to the rocks two hundred feet below.

'Come out, dogs! Come out.' Phil swore, and tried to call off the dogs. 'I'll lose them down there! Too steep . . .' We all stood and watched the terriers streaming down to the gulley after the fox, yelping and springing over the short grass. Guns were cocked and ready just in case the fox should turn back. When . . . 'Look out!' came a shout from behind us. And, turning round, I was faced with another fox running straight towards us from the same isolated gorse bush that had hidden the first! An odd terrier that had been dozing in the sun and missed the original excitement had woken to find its mates gone, and had smelt the original fox's scent. Back-tracking, it had stuck its nose in the bush that had harboured the fox. The result was the second fox ran right through the middle of the lot of us! Only this time guns were loaded, triggers cocked, and everyone was ready for the kill! *Bang . . . Crack . . . Boom . . . Bang . . .*

'Look out! He's dodging your way! Watch out, for Christ's sake! Damn and blast . . . Shoot 'im . . . shoot 'im . . .!' *Bang . . . Bang . . . BANG . . . BANG . . .* It must have been all over in less than thirty seconds and I was left, ears ringing, to look round to see the damage. By some extraordinary fluke nobody had even been hit, let alone killed. Talk about luck. There must have been a good forty shots fired as the fox ran through the group. I'd watched one chap standing on a rock who had blown a hole between his feet trying to get a bead on the animal as it ran within three feet of him.

'How on earth did us miss 'm?' said the owner of the Damascus barrels. 'Must have been the excitement.' And indeed they'd also managed to miss the fox!

'Excitement, my eye!' said Syd to me. 'That was the most dangerous exhibition of bad shooting I've ever seen. I'm off, Dan. If that's fox shooting, I'll stick to pheasants!'

It was clear from the first lambing that the foxes that infested the farm had to be controlled, and in the end my neighbour, David, and I managed the job with the help of Nick, a reformed poacher, who ran an agricultural merchanting business. We would patrol the top of the cliffs after dark in an old Land Rover, using a spotlight. And Nick's powerful rifle proved to be an efficient speedy way of dispatching the pests. Nick was a red-hot shot, and any fox within four hundred yards was a goner. I never got over the way we could find a fox in the middle of a field of ewes and lambs. The sheep would take no notice at all; they wouldn't even get up if it trotted within a few yards of them, whilst if it had been a dog they'd have gone bananas.

To add to the sport we'd pot any rabbits we came across with shotguns from the back of the Land Rover. A full team was four: a driver (usually David who knew the cliffs like the back of his hand and was fearless on the steepest slopes); Nick, who'd work the spotlight and keep an eye out for foxes; plus two 'guns' to have a go at rabbits. The fourth member of the party was often Gordon who had a share in the Land Rover with Nick.

Gordon was new to such basic country pursuits as night shooting, but he was as eager as anybody, and never shirked his share of paunching the rabbits at the end of the night – a pretty smelly and unpleasant business. The whole enterprise was a sort of mixture of *Boy's Own* and *Dad's Army*!

'Now then, Cherrington, which flank will you take?' Gordon was very keen to get things 'just right', and turned up in plus-fours with his gun in a proper case. But he was a good sport for all that. On this occasion we were going out onto the steepest part of David's cliff. I knew it, but neither Gordon or Nick had been there before. Not that it would bother Nick, he had no fear at all, and didn't mind how steep it got. But I wasn't too keen – especially hanging on to the downside on the back of the Land Rover as David jolted along the cattle tracks on particularly steep bits!

'Er . . . I'll take the right hand side, Gordon, if you'll take the left!' I knew which way David would drive. He liked being 'up the slope' in the driving seat if things were particularly difficult.

'Come on you two! For heaven's sake hurry up. The moon'll be up in an hour!' Nick liked it pitch dark for foxes. Gordon ignored Nick and proceeded carefully to fill his leather pouch with cartridges. He didn't like fumbling in his pockets for shells if things got lively.

'Gordon thinks we're going to war!' laughed David. 'But mind you, look sharp. There's far too many rabbits out where we're going and I'd like to see a score or more shot.' About half an hour later we drove out through a gate in the wall that divided the cultivated fields from the top of the cliff land. David had ploughed and re-seeded about twenty acres or so above the gorse and brambles over the last few years and it had grown well, but it was pretty steep.

'That was excellent sport, Cherrington,' Gordon said. We'd found half a dozen rabbits in the field we'd just left and Gordon had shot very well. They'd all been on his side of the Land Rover and he'd only missed one.

'What happened to the last one?' Nick asked rudely. 'You missed it by a mile.'

Nick was a bit fed up as we'd not seen a fox yet.

Gordon started to reply indignantly. 'I'd have shot it easily if you hadn't jogged my arm.'

Nick controlled the spotlight standing between Gordon and I as we leant forward over the cab of the Land Rover. 'Balls!' said Nick, and was about to add some other insult when David stuck his head out of the cab.

'Shut up, you two!' he said quietly. 'There's always a fox out here. I'll keep going and not stop to pick up any rabbits in this first bit. We'll turn at the end and pick them up on the way back, but you'll need to hang on, it's a bit steep. And there's the odd bump or two.' I got a firm grip on the Land Rover, knowing what was coming. But Gordon stood up with both hands on his twelve bore ready to pot any rabbits, and show Nick, what an 'ace' shot he was.

Well, David certainly got a move on! First of all he drove straight down the ever steepening slope with all the lights out. Then suddenly he swung right and switched on. The Land Rover teetered along across the slope and a dozen or more rabbits scuttered across in front of us heading for the line of gorse and safety below. I managed to get off two shots and bowl one rabbit over, but for the life of me I couldn't hang on and re-load at the same time! I'd just have to wait until we stopped.

'Shoot . . . shoot . . .' Nick was whispering fiercely, as we continued across the slope. 'For goodness sake SHOOT . . .' Rabbits flashed acoss our sights in droves, but I couldn't get a cartridge in. And Gordon hadn't shot at all. David stopped and switched off the lights and engine.

'What's up?' he whispered fiercely. 'Why aren't you shooting?'

'It's all I can do to hang on, Dave.' I said. 'You'll have to stop between rabbits.'

'I can't do that or the foxes'll be gone,' David whispered back. 'Look. Leave the rabbits. If we see a fox I'll chase him and you have a go with the shotguns. If we stop for Nick to line up with the rifle the fox will be in the gorse! You'll have to look sharp, mind.'

I turned to look across at Gordon in the gloom. 'Did you hear that?' Gordon gave a sort of strangled grunt, and I remembered he hadn't had a shot at a rabbit recently. 'Is your gun jammed or something?' This stung a retort from Gordon. 'How the hell am I supposed to shoot with this thing at forty-five degrees? It's all I can do to stay on board.'

'Oh, come on!' said Nick. 'It's not that bad! Shoot one-handed! Or are you too frightened?'

Whatever Gordon might have said it was lost in the jolt as David took off again, only this time he drove a good deal faster. I suppose I should have known that David knew what he was doing and that he'd decided to put an end to Nick and Gordon bickering at each other, but at the time it seemed he was intent on killing the lot of us! He drove on across the slope at what seemed breakneck speed. I lost all interest in rabbits, and simply hung on for dear life, waiting for the Land Rover to turn over! Even Nick hung on a bit tighter than usual, and I heard him mutter to himself 'Christ! this is getting a bit hairy!' Gordon was totally silent. And I could only imagine what it was like being on the down side of the Land Rover jolting and bouncing above certain death! Suddenly David shouted, 'Fox! Look, fox ahead. Hold tight, I'll get closer.'

I looked up miserably, and sure enough, there was a fox forty yards or so ahead racing down towards what looked like a precipice! Instead of pulling up David spun the wheel and put his foot down, intent on following the fox and taking us to meet our maker!

'Look out, David!' I shouted, 'we'll turn OVER . . .'

'Christ!' repeated Nick, 'Christ . . .' monotonously beside me. Then, just as we were about to plunge full steam ahead into the abyss there was a single shot from Gordon, and the fox slumped forward to skid and roll over and over down the hill, as dead as a Dodo . . . David stopped. 'Thank heavens for that,' I said quietly to Nick, who nodded agreement. David got out.

'Jolly good shot, Gordon. Must have been all of forty yards!'

'It's a matter of giving them enough lead!' said Gordon in a queerish voice, as he clambered down from the Land Rover to walk forward and inspect the quarry. 'Will there be any more out here?'

'No,' said David. 'That's it. We'll go on back now.'

'Thank God for that!' said Nick to me as we waited for Gordon and David. 'I don't mind it out here normally, but David did get a bit carried away back there. I know Land Rovers are good, but in the end it is possible to turn them over you know. Wasn't that a good shot of Gordon's? I thought he was in too much of a funk to shoot at all. Just shows how wrong you can be about a chap.'

On the way back Nick continued to congratulate Gordon on his remarkable shot and, all in all, it was agreed we had had a successful evening. Gordon gave me a lift home.

'Look, Cherrington,' he said as he dropped me off, 'I don't mind coming again, but let me know if it's going to be foxes on the cliff top again will you?' He paused. 'I don't mind telling you I was scared witless. Damned if I'd own up to Nick, though. That shot was pure self-defence! I knew if I missed we were all for the chop. I could no more do it again than fly to the moon. If it's to be out there again, I'll find a reason to cry off.'

IQ AND INSTINCT

My biology master had spent a great deal of time explaining to me that it was IQ that divided us from animals – the 'lower orders'. Fair enough, but all I can say is that over thirty years or so I've found plenty of smart animals.

Mind you, there's a difference between intelligence and training. Take foxes and electric fencing. I had been farming nearly twenty years when I found the answer to the problems of foxes at lambing time: it was all to do with animal intelligence. A friend of mine suggested trying an electric fence to keep foxes out of the lambing field. I must say I was pretty sceptical – foxes are supposed to be the most cunning of creatures. But it was spectacularly successful.

The fields on Netton are surrounded by Devon banks – earth banks about five feet high planted with thorns and gorse to make secure boundaries. My sheep didn't see things that way and treated them as natural obstacles to be tackled if there was nothing better to do! I'd had to fence both sides with posts and wire, and if you walked along these fences anywhere on the farm, you'd find foxes' tracks where the animals had gone through the square of the wire and then up and over the top of the bank. The whole farm was criss-crossed with these 'highways'.

I decided if the electric fencing was to work we'd have to put it on the lambing field side of the Devon bank. Fencing the opposite side was out, as this particular field was bounded on two sides by roads and tracks. So I put the single strand of electric wire about eighteen inches off the ground, two to three feet away from the bottom of the bank. John helped me roll out the wire late one afternoon, right at the start of lambing.

'Do you think this'll stop the foxes then, Dan?' he asked.

'I don't know,' I said. The single wire looked pretty useless; any self-respecting fox could simply hop over it. 'It's supposed to work. The idea is the fox is very wary of anything new and when he comes across this wire across his normal run, he stops to sniff it . . . then ZAP, he gets a good old belt from the fencer . . .'

'Never thought much of the old fencers we used to have,' said John, 'if you hung on tight you'd hardly feel it.'

I had just finished wiring up the fence to my secret weapon.

'Ah,' I said, 'this one's different. It's from New Zealand and it gives a shock of five thousand volts. The harder you catch hold, the worse it feels!' I connected the fencer to the old car battery that powered it and switched on; it made a pretty harmless tick . . . tick . . . tick . . .

'Sounds the same,' said John, and he reached out and touched the wire . . . _zap_ . . . 'Coo! Bugger!' John leapt back, shaking his hand. 'That's some shock! Even with my rubber boots on I felt that.'

We both looked at the fence with fresh respect. 'Maybe it'll work after all,' John said. 'Perhaps it _will_ keep the foxes out.'

'Trouble is, we won't know if it does work, John,' I said.

'How's that?' he asked.

'Well, how will we know if any foxes have actually been scared off unless we can see, and that's pretty unlikely in the middle of the night! Only way we'll have any idea is if we don't have any trouble with the lambs.'

John shook his head, doubtful of my logic: he'd been the one who'd touched the fence.

*

Next morning John came down to the farmyard from his early morning check of the lambing field. I could see the grin on his face from fifty yards.

'Here! . . . you'd better come quick, Dan . . . that 'lectric fence works all right! You come and see . . .'

'What do you mean?' I asked.

'Never mind, you come and see!' said John excitedly. We stopped the van short of the lambing field and I followed John quietly to the road gate. John stopped, and then he caught my arm.

'Look! . . . there! . . .' I looked, and then spotted the fox. He was perhaps three hundred yards away from us on the far side of the field, slinking along the fence line behind the peacefully grazing ewes.

'Well I'm damned!' I said.

'There were two here when I came up. I didn't notice them till I was halfway round the field. One ran through the fence – he gave a good old yelp as he went – I reckon he got a shock all right! This one went right up to the wire, but he wouldn't go through. I reckon they came into the field without noticing the wire and found the fence when they went to get out . . .' John talked as we walked across the field towards the fox. 'Look at that!'

The fox ran right into the corner of the field but stopped at the last moment, then turned and crouched, ears flattened, to look back towards us. Obviously it was terrified of the fence. In the end it did go through with a rush and a yelp when we were no more than thirty yards from it.

That was the end of our problems with foxes at lambing time . . . a simple electric fence was a hundred per cent better than all the traps, guns and hunts we had tried in the past.

The fear of the fox was 'training' rather than IQ, of course. A 'conditioned reflex' in jargon, I suppose, and I've had dogs that felt the same way about electric fencing. One was so bad that he simply refused to go into the field in which he'd had a shock;

and another that would wait for me to tell him whether the fence
was on or off before he'd go near it.

I came across a herd of goats in Australia, however, whose
attitude was entirely different – you'd have to call it intelligence.
I was on a farming trip looking at reclamation work in New
South Wales. The original settlers had simply burnt the native
gum trees and bush to try some simple cropping. They'd
brought their own weeds with them from the 'old country' and
this particular area was now cursed with a jungle of blackberry.
Spraying was expensive, and the stock farmers who now owned
the land had found a novel way to tackle the problem. They'd
cashed in on another of the pioneers' cast-offs and caught up
large herds of wild goats that roamed the open semi-desert area
two to three hundred miles inland. The areas to be reclaimed
were fenced into large blocks, and the goats let loose. Goats,
being goats, preferred the blackberry bushes to grass or clover,
and large areas had been reclaimed in this way.

'They're the very devil to keep in, Dan,' Ned, my host,
explained as we drove round. 'We use this high-powered electric
fencing. They really do respect it . . . mind you, we have some
problem if it ever gets switched off!'

'Why?' I asked. 'Surely, once the goats have been trained to
the fact that they'll get an electric shock from the wire, they'd
simply leave it alone!'

'Think so, wouldn't you?' laughed Ned. 'I'll show you if
we're lucky . . .'

We drove on round several thousand acres of Australian scrub
country in the process of being reclaimed, and I saw every shape
and colour of goat you could imagine. There was no attempt to
separate them into age, size or sex. They simply lived together
in herds of fifty to a hundred animals – billy goats, nannies and
kids altogether. I asked Ned if there was any money in the goats
themselves.

'Not worth a bullet,' he said cheerfully. 'Once we've finished
the job I'll just give them to a neighbour.' Suddenly, he stopped
the pick-up and turned off the engine. We were facing the

corner of a paddock, parked on a knoll looking down on a small herd of goats that were walking purposefully towards one of the electric fences. There must have been thirty or more goats in the herd – mostly nannies and kids – Ned wound down his window and said quietly, 'You watch this . . .'

The herd walked to within five or six yards of the fence, bleating quietly to each other . . . then they stopped. Nothing happened for a minute or so as they stood and looked at the fence . . .

'They know it's electric, then?' I whispered to Ned.

'They sure do,' said Ned, 'but they're checking to see if it's on. Just watch . . .'

One of the nanny goats at the head of the herd turned and deliberately nudged a young kid towards the fence. It stopped. The nanny butted it forward again gently, but firmly. It stopped again . . . again the nanny nudged it forward . . . the kid reached forward and touched the electric fence with its nose . . . 'Mehh . . .' it bleated and jumped convulsively away, well and truly zapped. The herd turned and walked unconcernedly away to find some brambles to munch, satisfied they couldn't get at the succulent morsels on the other side of the wire.

'Well I'm blowed!' I said.

'Yeah! They try that every day. If we have a fencer off for more than a few hours they're through and long gone! Marvellous how the old nannies make the kids try it out, isn't it?'

Mind you, goats are odd creatures. A shepherd on one farm I knew well had a goat called Shemesh that was all but human.

'What a mess, Panch,' I said, as the shepherd and I looked at the contents of his fridge on the kitchen floor . . .

'It's the blessed goat, Dan,' he said. 'She's nuts on butter. She waits for the Missus to come back from shopping and sticks her head in the shopping bag. If she smells butter, then look out! She can turn the knob on the outside door – open the latch on this one – although how on earth she knows the butter's kept in the fridge I don't know!' Panch shook his head indulgently and we went out to find the culprit. Shemesh was sitting on the broad windowsill of his Cornish cottage gazing intently through the window: a large white Sanen goat in the pink of condition, with a pucker leather-studded collar.

'Ha!' laughed Panch, 'watching TV again! Hey, Shemesh, what are you doing?' Shemesh bleated without turning her head.

'You're pulling my leg, Panch,' I said. 'Watching TV! I don't believe it.'

'She is!' said Panch. 'You watch. I'll go and turn it off.'

I stood behind Shemesh and looked over her shoulder at the flickering screen inside the room; it suddenly went blank. Immediately Shemesh bleated, then she began knocking on the window with a hoof . . . tap, tap, tap . . . After a minute or so Panch switched the TV on again. At once Shemesh stopped tapping the window and settled quietly to gazing through the glass!

Panch came out laughing. 'Well!' I said. 'I've never seen anything like that!'

'You should have seen the run around she gave us when we tried to get her in kid,' Panch said. 'It's pretty hard to know when goats are on heat, and they don't stay on for long. Well, we decided that we'd breed from Shemesh, so we took her up the road in the back of the pick-up to meet a billy a couple of miles away. But no joy. The owner of the billy told us what to watch out for, and as soon as we spotted Shemesh getting frisky we should drop everything and bring her. Well, she just liked riding in the back of the pick-up! The number of times she fooled us into thinking she was on heat!' Panch shook his head and looked fondly at the goat. 'Only one thing that really annoys me,' he said, 'she will eat lettuces. We try growing them in the garden. They just get going, when she hops in and scoffs the lot! It's no good fencing them either, she can jump five feet from a standing start! That's if she can hear the electric fence ticking! If it's not on, she simply walks through the wire!'

*

A couple of weeks later I dropped in to see Panch to find him sitting triumphantly by the back porch with a strange looking electronic gadget in his hand.

'I've cracked it, Dan,' he told me. 'Electric collar. This is the transmitter, and there's a receiver on Shemesh. I'm just waiting to train her to stay out of the lettuces.'

Shemesh was nibbling quietly at what was left of Panch's flower garden, and you could clearly see the bulky grey plastic collar she had on in place of her usual smart leather job.

'Have a beer, mate?' said Panch, pointing towards the last full can on the ground beside him among the pile of empties. He had obviously been at the training for some time!

When Shemesh had finished with the flower bed she strolled across to check on the lettuce patch . . . Yes, there were a couple worth a chomp! She hopped over the fence . . .

'No, Shemesh!' Panch said firmly, pressing the red button on the transmitter. '*Mehh . . .*' bleated Shemesh loudly, as the electric collar did its stuff, and she hopped out of the garden.

'Couple more goes like that'll train her for sure . . . Here, sit down, I'll get another chair.'

We started to discuss sheep. I watched Shemesh idly over Panch's shoulder. He glanced at her occasionally. After fifteen minutes or so I noticed the goat. It was watching Panch . . . and satisfied his attention was elsewhere, started sidling back towards the lettuces. If Panch turned to glance at her she'd stop, and stand looking vacantly around, innocent as anything. As soon as he looked away she'd take another purposeful step towards the garden. I was fascinated, and eventually the goat hopped the fence, grabbed a mouthful of lettuce and was out of the garden between Panch's glances. He never did manage to grow lettuces whilst Shemesh was around!

Generally speaking, sheep are not like goats, and show very little individuality, let alone IQ. Most of the year they live contentedly as members of the flock; quite literally following each other around for no better reason than the one in front is going somewhere. You'll see a whole line of them in a completely open field stop, and wait politely, whilst the leader tries to remember where it's going; the followers refuse to step off some invisible track to pass the one in front. This all changes at lambing time, and for about a month the character of the ewes alters completely. You can call it the mothering instinct if you like, but for a week or so they suddenly become individuals. The desire to have and rear an offspring takes over – often quite some time before they actually produce. When this happens they become 'pinchers'. These pinchers are a damn nuisance. They convince themselves they've lambed and steal any stray lamb they come across. When they actually produce their own, the one they've borrowed is rejected, of course. It's not always as simple as that. I had an old girl once who was convinced that motherhood was a sort of numbers game . . . she produced a twin of her own one evening, then spent all night causing chaos by trying to foster as many other lambs as she could. She had managed to find five extra when I found her, and sorting out who belonged to what was impossible . . . she didn't mind which you left her with, and the other ewes she'd stolen offspring from weren't much help; either sniffing suspiciously or butting whichever I offered them. In the end I had to put six ewes in the stocks, thanks to the over-developed maternal instinct of that one sheep.

The stocks were a device to try and convince reluctant mothers that the lambs on offer were indeed their own. The ewes were put in a four foot by four foot solid walled pen. They were then held by the neck in a slot in one wall so that their heads were on the outside. The lambs were then put in the pen and they soon found they could get at an ad-lib milk supply without the ewe being able to check if they were the right ones or not. The idea was that you left the ewe in the stocks for 48 hours, by which time she'd have forgotten what her own lamb ought to look like, or indeed how many she'd originally had. After 48 hours she'd accept the lambs as her own. This was the main way we'd use to try and fool ewes into accepting lambs, but it could be annoyingly unpredictable. Some ewes you just couldn't fool at all, whilst others were as easy as pie.

The easiest I ever had was a Welsh ewe from the cliff, whose overriding desire to have a lamb was quite extraordinary. Ewes that produce dead lambs at birth will clean them off and stay with them for hours. It's pitiful to see the love and affection they have for a scrap of dead skin and bones, and this particular ewe I found that morning even charged Scotty as we found her amongst the gorse.

'All right, Scotty,' I said, and he backed off a few yards to crouch and watch; keen for the order to catch the little Welsh ewe that was facing him so bravely.

'Well, born dead, eh?' I examined the small carcase, limp and bloodless. The ewe *bahhed* anxiously and came to within a few feet of me as I handled the body. What to do? The quickest way would be to fetch a spare lamb from the farm – bring it out, skin this one and try just leaving it with the skin on. It sometimes worked without penning up the ewe . . . But this lamb was so small. Its skin would only cover half a reasonable sized lamb.

First I'd better check to see if the ewe had any milk. Holding the lamb in front of me I put my crook on the ground. The ewe was so keen I caught her easily and turned her over on her backside. Yes, her udder was small but warm and firm – milk in both teats. I let her go. I'd catch her again with Scotty when I decided what to do. But instead of running away, the ewe stood her ground, sniffing anxiously at the dead lamb. Then she looked at me and *bahhhed* again. I wonder, I thought. I'd had a ewe with a twin last evening. They were no more than fifty yards away across the close-cropped cliff grass. The Welsh ewes never made much of a job of twin lambs anyway. I walked across to the twin. One was definitely not as big as the other – quite fit, but very small and fragile. I picked him up and popped him in the front of my jacket. His own mother, suspicious of Scotty and I, called to the second lamb, and as soon as it ran to her, she set off along the top of the cliff, not bothering to look back.

I walked back to the first ewe and knelt by her dead offspring, shielding the lamb from his mother with my body . . . A quick sleight of hand and live and dead lamb were exchanged. I stood up.

'Well, then,' I said, 'that's done the trick. Look, he's alive and well!' The lamb gave a small bleat, and as I stepped clear the ewe rushed eagerly forward. She sniffed the foundling and accepted it immediately. The lamb was of an age when one milk bar is as good as another, and that was that!

What helped in this case was, no doubt, that I'd found a replacement lamb quickly whilst the mothering instinct was strong in the ewe. I was also helped by the fact that Welsh ewes are not that keen on twins – the other ewe had been more than happy to lose half her responsibility. I've often seen a Welsh ewe try and get rid of one of a pair of lambs. As soon as the second one is born and cleaned off the ewe will start to walk away, looking back to call the lambs. The lambs, only minutes old, will stagger after her – the first born usually stronger than the second. The ewe will let the first lamb catch up and suckle her, then she'll set off again. She'll keep this up until the second lamb fails to follow, and is left to a pretty swift fate. I suppose this instinct is survival of the fittest – one strong offspring is better than two weak ones.

The habit was so common in the Welsh ewes I kept that if I found a new-born twin late at night on my last round, I'd hobble the ewe until morning, or use a screw-in tether that would keep the family together until daylight. Cross-bred ewes are totally different from the Welsh ewes, which is just as well as you're normally trying to fool them into accepting a second lamb, which is much more difficult.

Ewes certainly can count . . . at least, they know two is more than one, and once a ewe has had her single lamb, cleaned it off and it's suckled, they are hard to convince they've produced a second, even in the stocks. The best time is to catch them when they're lambing. If the flock is kept inside 24-hour surveillance it's easier.

There's always a 'pool' of unwanted lambs once you've started lambing: triplets or quads that are better split up, or the odd orphan. Most of the 'mothering-up' would be done at night. You'd spot a ewe lambing, and if she was a suspiciously healthy specimen you'd lamb her to see if she had a single (ewes that have single lambs don't have the same demands made on their metabolisms as multiple pregnancies, and are normally in better than average condition). If it was one only, then my method was not to let the ewe see her new-born lamb. I'd tie her up whilst I went for a 'spare' from the orphans box, or pinch a triplet from another pen in the lambing tent. Then I'd lay the ewe on her side again, put my hand gently inside her and go through the motions of 'lambing' to convince the ewe she'd produced number two. Then I'd rub both lambs together to get plenty of the slimy goo on the orphan – if the orphan was fit and well I'd sometimes tie its legs together. If, when you let the ewe up to examine her lambs one jumps up and rushes in for a feed like an express train, it can stretch credibility too far.

This method is pretty successful – the more patient and quiet you are, the better the chances; but one thing I found over the years was that the ewes were colour conscious. Putting a black and white lamb together was a recipe for disaster. OK if nature happens to do it, but 'no go' if I tried. I've seen endless other methods tried to fool ewes – nasal sprays that smell strongly of anything but lamb – blindfolding the ewe, and even one chap that used to swear by sticking the mother's head in a bucket.

Success could be transient. Some 'mothering ups' would appear to work – you'd send the ewe out to the field after a day or so, only to have intelligence override instinct, and the ewe would decide on one or the other as *the* one . . . she'd then become quite violent in her attacks on number two as it tried to get a feed. These rejected lambs would normally find their way back into the orphan box unless they became adept at stealing milk. These small thieves were extremely cunning, but they're easy to spot in the field. Characteristically they have dung on their heads, which comes from the way they get at the udder.

Instead of approaching the ewe from the front, they wait until a ewe is suckling her own offspring, then they dash in from the rear, reaching between the ewe's back legs for a quick suck. Hence the mucky heads from the ewe's bottom.

I once had a ewe that ditched one of her mothered-up twins no less than four times. She reared it in the end, although I can't say I won really! The first time John brought the discarded lambs back things were fairly quiet in the stocks, so I went and caught the ewe with her preferred lamb. Back she went into the stocks for 48 hours, then three days in a separate pen. All seemed fine this time, and when you checked over the gate the ewe would let both lambs suck. She'd also call for either lamb to be returned when you took them away in turn. So back she went to the field . . . Four days later John reported 'no go'. I decided this time I was not going to give up . . . damned if she'd beat me, so back she went through the system. This time I gave her three days in the stocks, and four days in an individual pen. We got to know each other quite well, and she'd eat nuts from my hand when I went to check her late at night . . . Out she went again. By the fourth time she went through the system, lambing was just about over, and when I let her out she was put into the small field by the house where I could watch her through the window. The first day was fine – she'd let both lambs suck, but she did seem to favour her original. I crossed my fingers. On day two I looked out to see her grazing quietly. I whistled at her and she called to her lambs sitting together under the sitting-room window. They ran to her and . . . *bump* . . . the blessed old ewe bashed the second lamb away!

I cursed at her stubbornness; the lambs were a month old, perfectly fit and well, but if I took the unwanted one from her I'd have to put it on a bottle as it was still too young to live on grass alone. I went down and outside. What could I do but give up? I called up Flash, the little bitch I used for close work, and went out into the front field. As soon as we came into the small meadow Flash dropped to her belly 'eyeing' the ewe. The ewe stamped her foot and stood her ground, protecting her lambs.

The lambs, greedy as ever, seized the opportunity and dived in for a drink. The ewe, sensing the unwanted lamb, flinched briefly, but then concentrated her attention on the dog . . . feeding continued!

I left Flash with the ewe for an hour. The little collie was never happier than eyeing sheep, and she'd have stayed all day if I'd let her. In the evening we went back again to a repeat performance. As soon as Flash appeared the ewe would let both lambs suck. If she was on her own she'd bump it away, so I kept the ewe on her own in a paddock near the farm. Flash got so used to the routine that I'd only have to say 'Go on then . . .', and off she'd dash, out of the yard and up over the bank into the paddock with the ewe.

Mind you, the ewe never did take to the lamb completely, and in the end it weaned itself, but by this time it was old enough to do so. Perhaps it felt it was being 'used' in some sort of long-term battle of wills rather than being treated like a lamb.

BADGERS

There have always been plenty of badgers on Netton. The best
time to see them is in the autumn – the cubs are threequarters
grown then and keen to 'sus out' their territory. They stray
quite fearlessly across the fields and around the barns, and it's
great to see them on the road late at night – fat, silky-skinned,
their coats seem to ripple independently as they run with that
peculiar rolling gait along the road ahead of you.

I got used to seeing them close to when I dried grain in the
corn barn late at night. The pits into which we tipped the wet
grain opened onto the road that ran beside the barn, and the
young badgers would come to feed on the grain that lay heaped
outside the doors – they'd take no notice of the noise of the
machinery and dust and heat from the dryer. In fact, they'd take
little enough notice of me either; and as often as not they'd
pause for an extra mouthful before turning to scamper off when
they heard me coming.

One colony live in a small wood between the farm and the
local village, but the biggest set has always been on the cliff. It
had been well hidden in an enormous patch of gorse and bram-

bles when I first came to the farm, but in my keenness to use every acre, I'd cleared the whole of the cliff land to establish grazing for sheep, and the large collection of holes and mounds that the badgers had made over the years was left exposed and open.

Experts told me the badgers would desert, as they liked privacy and wouldn't live in full view – well, so much for the experts! That was twenty-five years ago, and the set is still going strong. There must be thirty or more holes in an untidy area, covering half an acre or so. I've no idea how many badgers live there, but it must be several. They're pretty quiet in the winter and I guess they hibernate, even in our mild climate. Certainly the holes show no signs of fresh tracks, although the rabbits that co-habit with the badgers keep the entrances and paths well worn.

About the middle of March the badgers start spring-cleaning, hauling out great mounds of straw and sheep's wool and anything that's been used for the winter quarters. Then you start to see them about – lean and hungry, and keen to get a new year started.

I've always had a soft spot for badgers. They seem to mind their own business, if you mind yours; and because they're short-sighted you can often get quite close to them at dusk. They don't take much notice of lights at night either, and we'd come across them most times when we went 'lamping' rabbits. Soft spots are one thing, however, lambs are another. After five years or so I had established a flock of Welsh ewes on the cliff.

'Another lamb dead this morning,' John told me, after his early morning rounds. 'Same as yesterday – head bitten right off clean. Whatever it is, doesn't eat the lamb, just kills it.'

'Damn the thing!' I said. 'We'll have to do something about this. That's four in a week. Was it a single or a twin?'

'I don't know,' said John. 'I couldn't spot a ewe without a lamb, but it might be better if you had a look. I've left the lamb where I found it. It's about fifty yards below the fence, just above the big rock outcrop . . .'

It was just as John had said; the lamb had been killed all right. There was fresh red blood on the headless carcase. I checked the rest of the flock and there were no other signs of trouble. Ewes with new-born lambs moved slowly away as I walked round, but they'd obviously not been worried during the night. Not a dog then, I thought. Sheep can't stand dogs amongst them at night, and a sheep worrier causes as much damage by 'mis-mothering' the ewes and lambs as it does by killing.

Well then, not a dog; and I'd never seen a fox kill like that! They invariably bite a lamb on the back of the neck or throat, but not take its head off so cleanly – that meant a far more powerful set of jaws. It looked as though it must be a badger.

''Tis a badger all right. An old dog, I reckon. The old males get challenged by young ones every year, and in the end, as they slow down, they have to give way . . . These old boys often get kicked out of the set. They'll go "rogue" then . . . they're the ones that take chickens, you know; and, yes, they'll kill lambs just like that. Still got powerful jaws, they have. See that? He's chomped that off clean as a whistle!'

Old Joe knew the cliffs like the back of his hand, and I'd gone to see what he thought, and get some advice.

'Will he keep it up, Joe?'

'I reckon so, Dan. You'll need to either shift the sheep or kill the badger!' (This story happened before the Wildlife and Countryside Act of 1981 which made digging badgers illegal and killing them only legal with a licence.) The old male – and Joe was convinced that's what it was – had two more lambs that spring, and then, thankfully, the slaughter stopped.

'Could have been a fox, Mr Cherrington.' The local hunstman had called in to see if I'd allow him to go cubbing on Netton.

'Chomping off their heads like that? Would a fox have the power in its jaws to do that?'

'I don't know, sir, but your neighbour has had a fair bit of trouble this spring. We reckon we've found the earth, a vixen feeding cubs . . . they're the worst offenders. Why don't you come over and see for yourself? The lads are going to dig her out this morning.'

He was keen to convince me that hunting was the best way of keeping foxes down. I've never agreed with that. You'll always find more foxes in hunting country than anywhere else.

However, losing lambs was a serious business, and maybe I had been wrong about the badger! There just might be some evidence in the fox's earth, so I agreed to go along.

The 'dig' had got off to a bad start. ''Tis a badger's set. No fox ever dug a hole like that!'

'Nonsense. Cubs have been seen playing in the field just there. It may have been full of badgers once, but now it's full of cubs, for sure!'

I had joined five or six bystanders and we stood around as the organizers argued. The hunt terriers were as keen as mustard, whining and yelping, straining to be allowed down the gaping hole amongst the brambles at the edge of the wood.

'Are there any signs of dead lambs?' I asked.

'Dead lambs? Those little varmints will have cleared up every scrap, Mr Cherrington. We won't find any laying about, you know.'

I didn't argue, and in the end it was decided to let the terriers down the hole anyway.

It was always risky, if it did turn out to be a badgers' set, as a badger can easily kill a Jack Russell, or at least injure the brave little dogs very badly. Anyway, down went the dog, and for a while nothing happened. Then there was a real commotion from the hole . . . muffled barking and thumpings, until out came the dog bleeding from a nasty gash in the side. ''Tis a blessed badger! Look at the damage it's done to Jack! Us'll dig him out then!'

And so, filled with indignation at what had happened to the terrier, the organizers set about digging the badger out with enthusiasm. I wasn't keen on seeing the badger being made to pay for simply defending its own home, but I stayed on, and I must say it was worth it. (And before you switch off in disgust, it's not always human beings that have the last laugh!)

For quite a while it was just hard work, and I began to think that they'd have to give up empty handed and leave the badger in peace; especially when the sweating, red-faced chief pick-and-shoveller said he'd lost the hole, thanks to a cave in.

'Here! Try one of the dogs, but keep him on a lead. He'll find the hole in no time.'

One of the terriers was brought forward and let go in the fair sized trench that had been dug. A quick sniff . . . scrabble . . . then yelping and straining on the leash it uncovered the hole. The result was a mini explosion of yelps and barks and deeper growls. And the dog was dragged out . . .

'Look out! He's just here! Mind he doesn't lock onto you then . . . Damn badger! He'll take your hand off!'

Badgers were well known for the terrible power of their jaws. The bravest of the tormentors cautiously peered into the freshly uncovered hole to exclaim excitedly . . . 'I see him! He's just back there. Here! Give us the gun. I'll shoot him!' His assistant passed down an ancient ·22 rifle.

''Tis damn hard to see the blessed animal!'

The man strained to peer down the hole. But at last he fired. Once, twice . . . and then a third time.

'That's it,' he said, standing up with a satisfied grin, 'I got 'im! Henry? Come down and give me a hand to get him out . . .' With that, his partner in crime jumped down into the trench, and the more bloodthirsty bystanders craned forward for a better look. The man knelt down and put his arm right into the hole . . . when suddenly all hell broke loose . . .

'Help! He's coming out . . . For Christ's sake, look out! Let me out! He'll bite anything he sees! . . .'

The crowd erupted from the pit, gun tossed aside, and pick axe dropped, to scatter into the brambles, followed by a very large, very healthy, very cross, full grown badger. It was also a pretty intelligent badger, and, satisfied with its resounding victory, disappeared, at high speed, into the wood, before the diggers had a chance to re-group.

'I enjoyed that,' said a fellow bystander.

'Fox digging is one thing, but badgers don't do much harm, do they? . . .'

SMALL MIRACLES

One of the best things about farming is when things go right despite the odds; especially when it comes to animals. Take Jack, the first lamb born on Netton. He arrived a couple of days early, before we were really ready. I went out one morning to feed the flock and spotted a ewe on her own in the corner of the field. I had Scott, my number one dog, with me. 'Hey, Scott, sit down,' I said, 'you wait here, boy,' and I went quietly towards the ewe to see what the situation was.

'Hey, old girl, what are you up to then?' The ewe became aware of me and as she struggled to get up I could see that she'd been trying to lamb for some time. As she made it to her feet I saw what the problem was. It was what we call a 'headout'. The lamb's head had come out first and the legs had gone back as she was straining, trying to force the lamb out, and he was firmly stuck. What happens then is that the pressure on the lamb's neck from the mother's contractions blocks the flow of the vein that takes blood away from the head, but it doesn't stop blood continuing to be pumped in by the deep-seated artery – so the head swells up. In this case the lamb's head was the size of a child's football!

'All right, old girl,' I said and walked quietly towards the ewe to catch her. It was quite amazing that, even after ten or twelve hours of trying to get rid of a lamb, the ewe had enough energy left to run anywhere, but she set off at a determined trot, so I called up Scottie.

'Hey, Scottie, hold her!' and as quick as a flash Scottie was there, holding her firmly by the wool. I grabbed the ewe and told Scottie 'Let go, LET GO NOW.' He backed off reluctantly and crouched down to keep a stern eye on the situation. I turned the ewe gently on to her side. The lamb was stuck fast, its shoulders anchored in the pelvis and the head so swollen there was no chance of getting it back inside to try and get the legs and head to come together as they should. What I would have to do was to get my hand in to find a leg and bring it forward.

It's the sort of job the textbooks tell you is best left to the vet but at six o'clock in the morning in the corner of a field half a mile from the farm and telephone it is a question of 'needs must'. So I took my coat off, and set to work. The problem was that I had to get my hand inside the ewe whilst the lamb's neck was in the way, and once you get your hand through the pelvis and inside the womb of the ewe it is quite extraordinary how long the neck of the lamb seems to go on – it's rather like handling a snake! but as long as you know it has to be there in the end you find the shoulder of the lamb. Then you follow the shoulder down to its 'elbow'; once you find the elbow the idea is to get your finger behind it and then bring your hand out again through the pelvis trying to bring the lamb's leg with you at the same time.

In this case after a bit of a struggle I managed to get one leg right out alongside the swollen head but it was impossible to get my hand back in to find the other leg. So I tried a trick that I had been taught by an old Scotsman. He'd taught me that neither a ewe's pelvis nor a lamb are particularly round.

So the ewe pushed and I pulled and turned her at the same time and, after a minute or so, I felt the lamb suddenly start to come forward – after that it was easy and I soon had it out, its head so badly swollen that it took me more than ten minutes to make sure that he could breathe properly because of the size of his tongue. The ewe recovered remarkably quickly from her ordeal and she stood up and started to clean her offspring.

'Well, old girl,' I said, 'what are we going to do? I haven't got another lamb to put on you, and there's no way this little fellow is going to stand up and suck, not for while anyway.' I'd had these swollen-headed lambs before and it could take days for them to come to normal size and in this case the lamb really was grotesque. However much the old girl wanted him, I couldn't leave him in a pen with his mother whilst he was unable to lift his head from the ground. My neighbour David had started lambing some time ago and I knew he had a few spare lambs so I went up and fetched one of those to put on the ewe and 'Jack' as he was christened became the first orphan at Netton Farm.

Jack couldn't see for nearly a fortnight but he was bright as a button and once he managed to get his head off the floor and stop behaving like some demented Catherine wheel he began to take a real interest in life. When he heard someone coming into the kitchen he'd reckon it was grub time, and he'd struggle to get up – back feet first, then the front, and last thing to leave the floor of his box, in the corner by the Aga, would be his oversized head and he'd stand there swaying, trying to support its weight, with his little tail wriggling in anticipation of the feed that was to come. We never did find a mother for Jack; I suppose because he was the first, and such a game little fellow, he became part of the household. It wasn't until well into the summer when he started to eat flowers in the garden that he was banished to the fields with the rest of the flock.

The little triplet was hopeless from the start. He came from an old ewe who'd lost most of her teeth, so it was anybody's guess as to how old she was, but it must have been her tenth lambing, at least. She was a cross-bred ewe and she'd always put everything she had into producing her lambs. But despite having access to virtually ad-lib feed for the last month of pregnancy she was just too old for the job, and she'd lost a lot of condition herself. In these cases where sheep have multiple pregnancies the last foetus often dies before birth, in fact it can be re-absorbed completely. But in this case the ewe had somehow managed to keep things going. Her first two lambs were fine strapping animals. Because I'd been keeping a special eye on the ewe I'd helped her at lambing.

'Well now, what've we got then? Come on, old girl, just a wee push . . .' I always talk to sheep. Not that I think they understand the words but they certainly appreciate the sound of your voice. I'd spotted that the ewe had started lambing an hour or so before, and I'd penned her up in a nice large pen in the corner of the lambing tent. Now she had really got down to things and I could see the nose and front feet of the first lamb coming . . . The old girl wasn't that strong and she didn't try to get up as I came into the pen to check, so I decided I'd lamb her and get the job done quickly to get her on her feet again before she lost interest.

'Good girl . . . he's a beauty.' The first lamb came out long and slippery as an eel. Once I cleared its mouth of mucus it gave a convulsive breath and I put it under its mother's nose. Number two was also on the way out and I just helped gently.

'Not quite as big as the first, old lady, but a nice twin. Well done . . .'

I sat quiet beside her as she began cleaning the lambs, still laying on her side. Then she began to strain again . . . there were three! That was overdoing things a bit, I thought. I checked, and yes, tiny . . . but unmistakeable – two feet and a small head. I pulled the two legs gently forward and . . . snap! snap! I felt both go at once – the bones so soft and brittle that they had broken like tender young carrots. I eased the triplet out and there he was, no more than 2 lb in weight. By rights he should have died two weeks ago as the dwindling food supply had started to shut down. He was less than a quarter of the size of his brother and sister. What should I do? I'd had these little immature lambs before. If he'd been born outside in the cold

and wet he'd have died for sure. Similar ones I'd tried to keep
going in the past had never made it, unless they'd been single
lambs on particularly good mothers. Rearing them as orphans
had always had the same depressing result – they'd live for a day
or so and then go into decline and die – and this tiny scrap had
not one, but two broken legs as well . . . A quick tap on the
head? At that the little scrap shook convulsively and tried to
raise its head.

'It's so small, Dan. How on earth will it stand?' Sandy was
holding 'triplet' as I cut two small pieces from a plaster-of-Paris
roll. I'd brought the little fellow into the kitchen to give him the
treatment. Damned if I was going to let him die! First he'd been
given an ounce of colostrum, then, after a warm bath in the
sink, I'd borrowed Sandy's hair dryer to make him easier to deal
with.

'I can't leave his legs broken. I know he'll find it tough, but
unless we get them set he's no chance . . .'

'Triplet' was the model patient; quiet, beady black eyes
bright. It must have hurt like anything as I made sure the bones
were straight and in place, but he never made a sound. Both
breaks were clean – between the foot and the knee – but I plas-
tered both legs to the shoulder so they would be held still and
get a chance to heal. Sandy was right, the poor little chap
couldn't stand and was forced to lie in his box. He'd scrabble
convulsively if he heard anyone coming to feed him, but I never
expected him to make it.

Against the odds after ten days he was still alive – no bigger,
but still bright-eyed, and I decided to take the plaster off.

'Damn!' I said. 'One's OK but the other just hasn't healed at
all . . . oh dear, well, I don't know . . . maybe I'd better knock
him on the head . . .'

'You can't, Dan. He's such a trier. Look, why don't we try a
splint? He might be able to manage . . .'

Sandy and I had agreed that unless we could get 'triplet' on
his feet he wouldn't make it, but I wasn't too confident about
the splint idea. The leg had been broken ten days now and the

chances of it healing were not good, and whilst 'triplet' was still alive he simply wasn't thriving. But we'd come this far . . . I made the lightest splint I could from piano wire and gauze and crossed my fingers.

Talk about game, it took 'triplet' days to master getting round in his splinted leg, but at least he now had three that worked. The bad one he dragged gamely round for over a fortnight and at last he actually began to grow. In the end he became so active that I decided it was time to see how things were. If the worst came to the worst I could get Tony, the vet, to amputate the leg. Not that 'triplet' would have been worth anything as a three-legged sheep, but he certainly deserved to live.

But miracles do happen – sometimes, anyway – and 'triplet's' leg had healed. It was pretty weak and useless for a while but in the end he recovered the use of it completely.

The other 'miracle' when it came to 'lifting up thy bed' was Buster. I had one particular ewe that each year gave birth to a very large, single lamb – perfectly formed in every way but unable to get up. The first year it happened I kept her in for more than a fortnight. Whenever anyone was near her pen they'd pop in and hold the lamb up for a feed. The ewe got so used to this that she'd stand quietly whilst her offspring sucked. I showed the lamb to Tony the vet, who'd called in to perform a Caesarian. Tony took quite an interest and we tried various treatments, but all without success, and in the end we had to admit defeat and put the lamb down.

Next year was exactly the same – one fine big single lamb, but unable to get up. This time I took it away at birth and fostered two lambs onto the ewe. Perhaps if we reared the lamb with the orphans it would get the idea of walking from them. Also the orphans were looked after by Sandy, Ann and the girls, who had unlimited love and affection to offer. Maybe that would work. In the end I admitted defeat again and put the lamb down, despite the protestations of the orphan-rearing team. They had agreed with me there was no sign of the lamb getting up after a month and every treatment we could think of, and we decided it must be a genetic condition from the ewe.

The third year Buster arrived . . . he was just that, a great buster of a lamb, 14 lb at birth, vigorous and a great character, but, just like his brothers from previous years, unable to stand. I was disappointed and angry with myself. I shouldn't have bred from the ewe again. It obviously was a genetic fault in her. I looked at Buster in the lambing pen . . . was it worth one more try or would it be kinder to knock him on the head now? In the end I weakened, put off the evil day, I thought, and turned Buster over to Ann and my daughter Lucy who were in charge of orphans that year.

'He really tries to get up, Mr C,' Ann said, after a week. 'Isn't there some way we can help?' I'd gone to check out the orphans. I needed a candidate for a ewe that had lost a lamb that morning. Buster baa'd and struggled convulsively to lift his head on the off chance of another swig from the bottle.

'I don't know,' I said. 'Maybe we could try him in a sling . . .'

A sling is just that, four posts in the ground with a sack tied between them. Then you cut holes for the sheep's legs and pop it in, adjusting the sling so that the feet just touch the ground. I often use a sling to get ewes back on their feet after a difficult lambing.

Buster didn't like his sling at all. He couldn't see everything going on around him. Before, he'd been able to scrabble himself around on the ground to face whichever way he pleased. Now he had to face forward and he hated it. Particularly when he heard Ann or Lucy coming with his bottle. The result was he struggled a great deal of the time.

'He's using his front legs, Mr C, come and see.'

And sure enough Buster, after only three or four days in the sling, was pushing himself up and down on his front legs, probably from sheer frustration! Maybe he'd make it after all!

For the next three or four weeks Buster had all the help and encouragement Ann and Lucy could give. Lucy would come home from school and drag Buster out of his sling; he was growing all the time and weighed a good 30 lb by now. Then she'd spend literally hours trying to get him to stand up on all four legs. Buster was as keen as Lucy and he'd try and try, but although his front legs were now pretty well a hundred per cent, the back ones simply refused to respond. I decided to broach the subject of failure . . . 'You can't, Dad, you just can't . . . Look, isn't there some way we could make Buster a wheelchair or something. At least he could get round a bit?' Lucy was adamant and close to tears. I capitulated, resigned to having Buster around as a cripple for the forseeable future.

I cannibalized an old pram and made Buster a sort of mobile sling. Buster thought it was great and soon gave it all his energy, but there was one major problem: he could get the pram to go forward all right – not always in a straight line – but he was incapable of going backwards! However big an area you set him off in the result was the same. You'd hear Buster baaing to be rescued and you'd find him with his head stuck in the hedge manfully struggling to keep going. After Buster had wrecked a flower bed or two and fallen down the garden steps, he was banned to the front field and for the next week or so you'd spot either Ann or Lucy, with endless patience, going to set Buster off on another run. They never gave up, and nor did he, until at last the miracle happened, and he started to use his useless back legs.

At first it was a flushed and breathless Lucy who demanded that I come and look at Buster. He was out of his sling, and after an age of coaxing he stopped his enthusiastic struggling long enough to stand, swaying wildly, on all four legs before falling flat on his back. Then there were more days of endless patience. Buster could stand all right if you set him up, but if he tried to move he'd fall over, and be totally unable to get up again – and he hated that – you could see his frustration and enormous determination to walk. I decided to put him back in his original sling, suitably modified for his increased size. He still hated it, but it did the trick in the end. Whilst he was in the sling he would struggle to be free and this built up the muscles in his back legs which had been useless since birth. Eventually the sling therapy and more endless patience made Buster able to get up onto his feet without help. Then, after nearly three months, Buster walked.

Eventually, that autumn, he went back with the flock. You'd spot him sometimes as the dogs rounded up the sheep. Buster had no fear of dogs, but the excitement of everyone else running meant he'd lose his concentration and his back legs would let him down. He'd go flying, head over heels, but then he'd struggle up and shake himself and get going again.

Buster proved something to me – with enough love on one side and never-say-die determination on the other, you can do just about anything.

FARM BIKES

I'd been farming fifteen years or so when I decided I ought to diversify; well, that's not strictly true, what actually happened was that I went off on a sort of study tour of New Zealand and Australia and I saw an idea that I was certain would take British farming by storm – if only they knew about it. I knew nothing about selling to farmers but I'd been on the receiving end long enough – surely if I managed to get it right they'd be queueing up in their hundreds and I'd be rich.

The earth-shattering idea I'd spotted was farm motorbikes. OK, so there was nothing new in the idea of using motorbikes on farms. I remember in 1959 being given a motorbike to go and round up sheep in Australia. This was on a sheep station next door to Woomera, the rocket-testing range. The sheep station was divided up into enormous fields, or paddocks as they called them. Each paddock was 5,000 acres or so in size and the land was very nearly flat. It was dry country, but there were scrubby trees that grew about twenty feet high, and what with these and the dry grass, you could only see a couple of hundred yards. This made finding the sheep, which were as wild as hawks, pretty difficult, as they had an area the size of a small town to hide in, and if they heard you coming, they simply ran off before you spotted them.

The manager used this trait to his advantage, and that's where the motorbikes came in. At each shearing time there was a gang of us hired to round up the sheep. We each had an old BSA motorbike – fixed wheel, no gears, no exhaust, no brakes, and a couple of lengths of rope with old tin cans tied on, preferably filled with stones. The idea was that a half a dozen of us would start from the gateway in one corner of a big square paddock – we'd follow the fence until we came to the opposite corner then we'd charge up and down in lines at right angles to the entry gate, gradually working back across the paddock. It was great fun, and only dangerous if a piece of dead timber got jammed in your back wheel. We never had a clue exactly where we were, you simply turned round and headed in the opposite direction if you found a fence; I personally never saw a sheep, and the noise was terrible. Eventually we'd find the gate again and report to the chap left as a 'counter'. If enough sheep had come through the gate, fine (within 10 per cent of what should have been in the paddock was considered successful); if we failed to chase out enough we'd go for another try.

All well and good, but these old BSAs had been no more than a fond memory for twenty years – it was in New Zealand that I met their successors. The ingenuity of the Kiwis coupled with the enthusiasm of the Japanese for a new market had produced motorbikes that were not just called farm bikes – they really were. They had knobbly tyres and very low gears (that meant they'd go anywhere), and a platform on the back for the dog to ride on. There were bikes with spadelug wheels – solid metal – for really tough going in the mud. They pulled trailers full of hay or a couple of sheep. They pulled mowers that cut thistles. You could put them on stands and then use them to drive shearing machines. Every farm I came to had a farm bike; they had even invented a form of 'foot bike' a cross between football and polo played on farm bikes, but this was pretty unpopular with the bosses as the normal result was a crop of broken legs.

I was completely sold, and as soon as I got back to England I rang all the importers of Japanese motorbikes. None of them had ever heard of farm motorbikes, let alone had any plans to import them. What an opportunity! Thank heavens I'm in time, I thought, so I refused to take 'no' for an answer. In the end Suzuki G.B. succumbed. They had a sales director called Maurice who was as keen on motorbikes as anyone.

'How many do you think we can sell, Dan?' Maurice wanted to know.

'Well,' I mused, 'there are 125,000 farms in Britain. If we can't sell 10 per cent of them farm bikes in three years, I'll eat my hat!' I could see Maurice's mind working overtime. Ten per cent of 125,000 is 12,500; at £300 a time, that was £3,750,000. Even if my estimates were wildly out, it had to be worth a go. In the end I convinced Maurice that he should get an initial consignment of 400 bikes and that the best way to sell them would be through agricultural machinery dealers. We'd set up a whole chain of dealers through the country and I convinced both Maurice and myself that I was the man for the job – I'd get a commission on each bike sold – £6.75 each, I believe it was.

Heaven knows what I thought I was up to, but I hired a Transit van and, armed with a whole stack of 'Yes, I'm interested' reply-paid cards from an advertising campaign, I set off round the British Isles. The first thing I found out was that the machinery salesmen who I'd always found so eager to please when they tried to sell me a new tractor, didn't suffer fools gladly. I started in Gloucester.

'Farm motorbikes! Who on earth wants a farm motorbike – all my customers drive Rolls Royces or Bentleys . . .'

'Ah, but it's the shepherd on these big estates that'll ride a farm bike.'

'You must be joking! No self-respecting shepherd I know would give up his Land Rover for a motor bike!'

'So you're not interested?'

'I didn't say that – they could have a place. How safe are they as Christmas presents for farmers' sons who have everything else?'

'They are not a toy, sir,' I said as I walked out.

*

I tried on the Welsh Borders.

'Farm motorbikes, boyo! Oh no, not round here – too mean to change the horse more than once every twenty years – can't even sell a tractor that's not at least third hand, can we?'

In the end I found a ploy that did sell a few to dealers, although it took time. I'd ring all the 'Interested-farmer-200-acres-or-more' replies in an area, sort out the schoolboys and cranks and find a couple of farmers who were interested. By now I didn't mind whether they wanted to keep the farm bike in the barn until it became a valuable antique or use it for shopping if the traffic got busy, so long as they'd buy one. Once I was pretty sure of a sale or two I'd check who they dealt with and *then* go to the dealer.

'Look, sir, Mr Bloggs is a customer of yours. Right?'

'Well, yes.'

'Then why haven't you sold him a farm motorbike?'

'A what? Does he actually want to buy something? Amazing.'

Then I'd take an order for six bikes, leave a couple of stacks of free literature and on to the next.

It actually got easier the less my conscience troubled me . . .

First: 'You say Frobishers of Derbyshire are taking on farm bikes?'

'Yes, Mr King, couldn't wait to get their order in . . . now will you take six or seven?'

Later: 'You say Kings are into them?!'

'Yes, Mr Frobisher. They ordered six this morning!'

I should have known that pride comes before a fall when I ran into a few problems in the on-farm testing bit. The idea of having a bike in the Transit van was that I could take it onto the farm and put it through its paces. I had a trailer as well and the idea was to have a gentle ride around the flat field or two with a couple of sheep up in the trailer, or go it alone over the hills to show just where the thing would go . . . My come-uppance came about twenty-five miles from John O'Groats. I'd only had two 'interested farmer' replies from Caithness – one a schoolboy and the other a demure sounding farmer who said, 'I would hate you to waste your time, Mr Cherrington, it was only idle curiosity that made me write in . . . but if you're quite determined, come by all means. It will have to be on the understanding that it's without obligation on my part though.'

I reassured Mr McM. that I was no Johnny-come-lately selling goods from the back of a van – this was purely a demonstration. The nearest machinery dealer in the area was at Wotton, near Wick. Two brothers who were kindness itself, but both pretty dubious about Mr McM.

'He's not best known for taking to innovations, Mr Cherrington. Three hundred pounds for the wee bike, you say? It does sound a bit dear for Mr McM.'

Mr McM.'s house was about five miles from Wotton and his farm was level fields in the small coastal plain. The land was not particularly good but it looked a lot easier than trying to ride up the side of a Welsh mountain where I'd been the week before.

One of the brothers had come with me.

'Good morning, Mr McM., this is Mr Cherrington. He's come all the way from Devon to show us his wee bike!'

Mr McM. didn't encourage at first sight – not that he was shifty or anything, but he refused to look me straight in the eye. He spoke with his gaze firmly in the distant hills. I'd got the bike out of the van ready for action, when he said vaguely, 'So that's a farm bike . . . I see . . . Do you think it could go across the field in front here?'

I looked across the road. The field was a nearly flat permanent pasture field, no real growth yet at the end of March, a few sparse rushes and the odd dead thistle. Some vague disquiet made me nervous.

'What do you usually use to get around, Mr McM.?'

'I use a horse, Mr Cherrington, very sure-footed and reliable. I find my horse gets around that field very well.'

'Mr McM.,' I said satisfied, 'this Suzuki farm motorbike will go wherever your horse might *and* it won't ask for a bucket of oats if it's not working!' With that I hopped on and went down through the gate and across the field, careful to go quietly with the same sort of dignity Mr McM. would expect from his faithful horse . . . then *puddddd* . . . The motorbike sank gently to its seat in a black peaty bog, coughed once, and died, leaving me stranded. In the end Mr McM. got out a tractor and pulled us out . . .

'I did'na think your wee bike would go across there, Mr Cherrington,' he said as I left. 'I think I'll stick to my horse.'

Funnily enough that marked the beginning of the end for my first excursion into selling. As I drove the eight hundred miles or so back to Netton, having been made a fool of by McM. hurt nearly as badly as thinking of the £6.75 I would have made if he'd actually bought one!

Shortly after that I was summoned to Suzuki by Maurice . . . 'I'm sorry, Dan,' he said, 'we're simply not selling farm bikes fast enough. We've decided to discontinue the idea.'

I remember being bitterly disappointed at the time. Blast Suzuki, I thought. They can't see a good idea when it's staring them in the face.

Fifteen years later farm bikes are a fact of life in Britain, but they're either Hondas or Kawasakis, and are mainly four-wheelers now and they've never been accepted with the same enthusiasm as they were in New Zealand. Perhaps it's the weather, or maybe British farmers really are too well off at the moment.

TVP

When I first went to Devon it was a long way from anywhere else. There was no M5, or any dual carriageways to speak of, and in farming terms the West Country was pretty isolated. This has always made it tough for anyone trying to sell anything unless they were actually based in the area. I learnt about sales reps pretty quickly. The first deal I did was to buy a load of fertilizer at full retail price without asking for a discount. Father pointed out the error of my ways.

'It's easier to save money by not spending it in the first place, Dan,' he said. I took this rather confusing advice as gospel, and went through a period of even asking for a discount on the purchase of a pair of trousers or meal at a restaurant.

Quite a few of the chaps who sold what I needed became friends (there were no sales ladies in those days and 'sales persons' were still a long way off). Life on a farm can be pretty boring, and the chance to stop for a cup of coffee and a chat was always welcome. It's all changed now, of course, nobody can afford to send a salesman off for a day's driving round the countryside if all he managed to get rid of was a few bottles of lamb tonic and a bag of dog biscuits.

I did business with two or three reps in particular. One was

Brian, who dealt in fertilizer, and led me astray more times than I care to remember. He'd turn up about 4.30 p.m. (particularly in the winter) and after half an hour or so haggling over prices, out would come the whisky; if I didn't produce a bottle, he would. By the time we'd finished one it seemed a pity not to have a crack at another! Brian would protest that he had to go until about nine, then he'd settle down for supper, ring his wife and stay the night. Brian was unusual in that although he worked for a national company, he stayed put for twenty-five years or so. He liked South Devon and simply refused to move. Most of the reps for the large firms served much shorter terms in Devon and Cornwall. You 'did your time' in the sticks and then moved on up the ladder. This meant a continual stream of earnest young men all desperate to get on and willing to have their legs pulled to get an order.

Peter worked for a company called RHM who specialized in animal feedstuffs, and he was particularly keen. He decided on a bold and imaginative way to capture a few more customers. He called one spring afternoon and introduced himself.

'I'm arranging a trip up to company HQ, Mr Cherrington. I've been told you're an "innovator"; I'm sure you'd benefit from a visit to our research labs . . .'

An 'innovator'? I guessed this was a snide reference by one of my neighbours to one of my ideas that hadn't quite worked out. But still . . . research *was* the way forward.

'How much will it cost?' I asked.

'Nothing. Nothing at all. The whole day's on RHM!'

A free day out! 'Tell me more,' I said, 'and you'd better call me Dan.'

'Well, we're organizing two buses. One will be coming up from Cornwall and the other from South Devon. Company HQ is in High Wycombe. We'll get there at about eleven for Brunch. Then tour the labs and research facilities. In the afternoon we'll visit a research farm, then we'll stop at a pub on the way back for pasties and beer.'

'Pasties and beer! I'm on,' I said. The only thing I wasn't too sure about was what Brunch was, but I guessed that eleven in the morning would make it something between breakfast and lunch. Still pretty confusing, as in Devon the midday meal was dinner, and lunch was a vague snack that posh people had. Perhaps I should have explained this to Peter – it might have saved RHM considerable embarrassment. I asked David if he was going when I saw him later that day.

'No,' he said. 'I used to get away quite a bit with the young farmers and it's more than my life's worth to go anywhere near London unless the wife's with me!'

'Ah,' I said, 'that's a pity. I'm not sure I'll know too many people on the trip.'

'Don't worry, Dan, about half of them will be cousins of mine. I'll tell a couple of them you'll be on the bus.'

David was right. Farming is a small world, particularly in Devon, and he was related to just about every other farmer I met. I shouldn't have worried about being left out of things as once we got under way the bus trip was great. Everyone was friendly, and there was plenty to discuss as we looked at the farming we saw on the way up the A303.

I was able to put in my twopenny worth as we crossed Salisbury Plain where I'd been brought up. I was sitting next to a Cornish farmer from Liskeard by now. We'd met the other bus on the way up and changed places so we could get to know everyone.

'Hundred-acre fields! You'm joking, Dan! My farm's only one hundred and twenty acres altogether!'

'Well, that's what they are, Mr Thomas. Mind you, until the war the land wasn't much use except for gorse and rabbits, but now, with modern farming, it's just about all been ploughed up.'

Mr Thomas shook his kindly head. ''Tis marvellous, but 'tisn't natural, young Dan . . . You'd best come down to Liskeard and us'll show you how to farm in proper fashion . . .'

Eventually we came to High Wycombe and the HQ of RHM. We shuffled out of the buses and strolled around in front of the imposing office block, stretching our legs, as Peter tried to get us organized to meet the nobs.

'This is Mr Smith . . . (or whatever his name was) Head of Research.'

Mr Smith coughed. 'Welcome to High Wycombe, gentlemen. I trust you had a good trip?'

''Twas long enough anyway,' said a voice from the back. 'Us is ready for this 'ere "Brunch" you'm telling of.'

We'd all been given a printed programme . . . Welcome by Mr Smith, then Brunch, then an address by one of RHM's big bosses. I should explain that, although RHM were now big in animal feeds, they were originally millers. In fact, the initials stood for Rank, Hovis, McDougal – you know, Home Pride, and all that. They were a very research-minded company and were world leaders in alternative uses for cereals. I was particularly keen to see their experimental plant that fed wheat to fungi then spun the fungi into strands of edible protein . . . but that would have to wait until after Brunch.

'Proper. That's what this is. Proper. Here, pass some of that there pâté.'

'Any more wine needed here?'

Peter stopped at our table, flushed and busy. His day out was turning into a real success. This was the sort of entente that built real customer loyalty.

'Wine? Much more wine and us'll start singing, Peter. But, well, seeing as you've opened the bottle . . . What do you call this? Hock, is it? Proper stuff, proper . . .'

After the pâté and toast we were looking forward to something more substantial and we weren't disappointed – chops, cabbage, potatoes and lashings of thick juicy gravy, literally covering everything.

'Another chop, Mr Thomas?' enquired Peter. Mr Thomas smiled and burped gently as he sipped his wine. 'I couldn't, Peter. I'm repleted . . . if I has any more of this 'ere Brunch, I won't be ready for dinner time . .'

Mr Thomas paused and looked at his watch. ''Tis nearly twelve already and us always has dinner 'bout one.'

Peter smiled uncertainly. 'We aren't having any dinner today, Mr Thomas.'

Mr Thomas laughed. 'I'm just pulling your leg, lad. This has been a proper welcome . . . proper! Well done.'

Peter blushed with pride and pleasure. Having your leg pulled by a Cornish farmer meant real acceptance.

'Er . . . welcome to High Wycombe. On behalf of RHM we would like to extend a warm welcome . . .'

The big nob was very impressive – grey suit, white shirt and cufflinks. Pink cheeks, freshly shaven . . .

'I do trust you've enjoyed your Brunch?'

'Proper,' we chorused, and I sneaked another refill into Mr Thomas's wine glass. The big nob smiled. 'You see, we thought we'd give you a little surprise . . . You see, you haven't been eating any *meat* . . .'

No meat! I looked at Mr Thomas. 'Nonsense,' he said loudly, 'proper bit of pâté . . . And that chop . . . as good as any I get from my pigs.'

'Oh no,' said the big nob excitedly, 'you see we make it all here out of wheat. It's called textured vegetable protein – TVP for short – we feed the wheat to a fungus then spin the fungus into a sort of artificial meat. I'm sure you'll agree it's every bit as good as the real thing!' He beamed at us.

'Artificial? Rubbish!' said Mr Thomas a bit grimly. 'What about my chop bone then? I suppose you spin that as well?'

'No, no,' said the big nob triumphantly, 'the chop bone is made of plastic!' A deathly hush fell on the assembly . . . plastic bones . . . artificial meat!

Mr Thomas examined the debris on his plate with great deliberation, then looked up, his face set like stone.

'Well then, Mr High and Mighty RHM, you'd better find a good market for your TVP and your plastic bones. This is the last time I want to see any of your chaps on my farm. Us produces the best meat in Britain and this 'ere rubbish is just a cheap trick, and I, for one, don't think it's funny.'

And that was that.

UNCLE ROBERT

Fathers are essential when it comes to getting started in farming. But having someone else older to bounce ideas off before making a fool of yourself is a great help. Uncle Robert wasn't actually my uncle – he was my godfather. He'd been a friend and mentor to my father when he'd first gone farming in Wiltshire and was only too happy to help me in my turn.

Uncle Robert had come to the chalk downs from the Midlands during the Depression. He was a stockman through and through, and his knowledge of sheep and cattle was second to none. His wife Aunty Kitty had the brightest, darkest eyes – they really were piercing – but she had a kind chuckle, and although as a small boy she frightened me a bit, I was always fascinated to go and visit them. Aunty Kitty's maiden name had been Wales and she had been so determined not to lose it that she married Robert Wales when she met him. Soon after they were married Aunty Kitty was crippled and confined to a wheelchair for the rest of her life. She refused to suffer fools and was sharp as a razor, and a housekeeper and my Uncle Robert looked after her between them.

Because they could have no children and Aunt Kitty wasn't up to travelling, Uncle Robert decided that rather than having to extract the last penny from farming he would simply enjoy it.

He bought a farm in Wiltshire when prices were rock bottom. Whilst he was looking he actually bid on a farm my father ended up with twenty years later. The farm was a thousand acres, more or less, and was on the market for £4,250. Uncle Robert bid £3,900 which was turned down. A year later the agent said that an offer of £4,100 would be acceptable. Uncle Robert offered £3,950 but refused to go any further, so that the deal fell through for the sake of 15p an acre. The last time the farm was sold it made between one and two million. Uncle Robert settled at Scotland Lodge near Amesbury; again this had about a thousand acres, and instead of ploughing the downland pastures to grow barley, he established a system of self-sufficiency derived from his farming background in Northamptonshire. He had a breeding herd of beef cattle which was based on old English Longhorns, and a flock of Jacob sheep. Both the sheep and the cattle were crossed with whichever breed Uncle Robert fancied trying, and the results were extremely varied. He had cattle of every colour combination you could imagine, including some with big round black spots like Dalmatians. The sheep were just as interesting: black-and-white Jacobs with up to six horns and crossbred offspring, usually all black but sometimes white, or off shades of grey. For all their colourful appearance Uncle Robert's stock were no joke, and his lambs always got top price in Salisbury market. The cattle he bred were kept on Salisbury Plain for two and half to three years, then he'd sell them to friends from Northampton where they'd go for fattening.

I suppose I really started to appreciate Uncle Robert when I went to university; learning the theory and most up-to-date farming methods gave me something to talk about. Father tended to drop off if I tried out a new idea on him after Sunday lunch, but Uncle Robert's normal smiling face would become completely serious as we discussed the rights and wrongs of a new breed of sheep, or whatever. At the time I was studying, there was a new method of getting the maximum production from grass called creep grazing. The idea was that you divided the grassland area for your flock of sheep into six paddocks.

Then you put special gates into the fences which allowed the little lambs to 'creep' in front of their mothers, so enjoying the best fresh grass whilst still being able to nip back for a quick drink from Mum when they felt like it. I was very taken with this idea despite a few teething problems they'd had on the college farm.

The worst problem was that the experimental field was next to a main road and well meaning people were forever stopping to go and open the gates so that the poor worried mothers could be with their dear little lambs! However, we didn't have any main roads at Tangley and I tried to persuade Father . . .

'It means we could carry six ewes per acre, Father. That would be four times the output we're getting at the moment.'

'I see,' said Father (who was into broad-acre farming with as few problems as possible). This was his only comment on the subject.

I decided to explain the system to Uncle Robert. At least he was willing to listen to new ideas, even if he was one of the older generation.

'Because the lambs always get fresh grass they don't get parasite problems . . . and you can tell when they're getting big enough for market when they have a job to squeeze through the special "creep" gates.'

Uncle Robert nodded attentively but said nothing.

'It's a brand new system, you see,' I went on. 'We've got this New Zealand professor who brought it from his last college,' I finished. 'What do you think, Uncle Robert?' I asked. 'Will it catch on?'

Uncle Robert smiled, and went to his desk. From a cubbyhole he produced a scientific report . . . 'Rotational Creep Grazing Trial . . . Scotland Lodge, Wiltshire . . . 1936' – before I'd been born!

'Don't be upset, Dan,' he said kindly. 'The trial failed to work for several reasons, one of which was a build-up of parasites that modern animal medicines would control. But it's interesting how little is really new in farming, isn't it?'

'Will it work now?' I asked.

'Well,' said Uncle Robert, 'I don't think so. You see land is still cheap enough – it's easier to buy more acres than use them intensively. Also if we all farmed like that, what would we do with the lambs?'

I saw Uncle Robert's farming with fresh eyes after that. His system was simple. He kept the number of stock the farm could carry without buying in any feed. He used no fertilizers except basic slag, and of the thousand acres he only ploughed enough to have barley, oats and straw to feed the stock through the winter. Over half the downland was never ploughed. In summer it grew more grass than the animals could eat, but because it was slow growing and unforced with artificial manure, this would keep and be eaten off through the winter. In the spring the down was grazed as bare as could be – not really starting to grow away until late April.

'You won't be able to afford to farm like this,' Uncle Robert would tell me, as we walked round. 'You see Aunt Kitty and I need very little.' Then we'd stop, perhaps to look at his Suffolk breeding sheep. 'Now, maybe you could do with a couple of rams, Dan? I've picked these out for you. They were late born last year but I haven't forced them on. I think you'll be pleased with them.'

At that time I bought thirty or forty rams a year for the various farms I was concerned with, but Uncle Robert's I kept for myself. Compared with the pampered and showy rams from Wilton Fair down the road they looked drab and ordinary, but after a year at home they were always the best, strong and lasting. Uncle Robert's philosophy was to let nature take its course and not push things or waste them.

'Look at that old boy'. He pointed out an example. I looked at an ancient Dorset Horn ram hobbling along on three legs. 'Hurt his leg fighting ten years ago on a neighbour's farm. The manager wanted to send him to the knacker . . . complained he was the most expensive failure he'd ever had. Cost twenty-five guineas as a ram lamb . . . I paid just two pounds for him, Dan.

He's bred over five hundred lambs for me that have topped the market in Salisbury every year!' Uncle Robert laughed. 'Good job old ones like me and my chaps don't get thrown out as quickly . . .'

Uncle Robert ran the farm with a foreman of 85 and two workers – one older than the foreman. Uncle Robert was in his late seventies, and only the shepherd, Billy, was under 50 . . . 'Average age of over 70, Dan, but we still get by!'

The old downland area was four hundred acres or so of permanent grass. The rest of the farm was ploughed and reseeded on a pretty leisurely ten-year cycle. The old down was a wonderful place. In March it was bare and grey – the constant nibbling of the sheep having cropped every sign of fresh growth to nothing. Then, when spring came, it would gradually come alive. First the tender young grass – Sheep's Fescue, Clewing's Fescue, Crested Dogtail – some Bents and Sedges in the coarser parts, but no Cocksfoot or rye grass. These grasses would dominate the early growth but as the growth outstripped the appetite of the lightly stocked sheep and cattle the grasses would send up seed heads and the wild flowers would appear. By the end of May the area would be quite unique – an oasis in the midst of all the wheat and barley and modern farming of Salisbury Plain. I once asked Uncle Robert if the whole of Salisbury Plain would have been like it before modern farming took over – an oasis of orchids and cowslips amongst the thistles and charlock that arable farming encouraged. As always, when you asked him a question on a favourite subject he laughed, 'No, Dan, I don't think so,' he said. 'If you want to see the natural downland, then look over the fence at the army land – all coarse grass and only small areas of what the naturalists would call "chalk downland" where there are enough rabbits to eat it down.' Then he pointed out to me distinct lines or furrows in the downland area we were walking across. 'You can see this is all pretty recent. Look, these are the old plough lines. All this area was under the plough in the Napoleonic wars.'

Indeed I could see them in the late May sunlight. The down-land at Scotland Lodge was Uncle Robert's own creation. Thankfully he left it for conservation so no keen young man with a wife and family to support could plough it up to cash in on all that fertility.

Uncle Robert died as quietly and peacefully as he lived, but ten years later I realized how little he and his philosophy of farming were understood or remembered.

I work for television from time to time, and was asked to take part in a conservation programme. You know the sort of thing: 'Why can't we all be concerned and *understand* the countryside?' A pretty well-known 'authority' on nature and conservation came to interview me; in kindness I'll call him Bob . . .

'What the programme is trying to do,' said Bob, 'is to show how important it is to save unspoiled natural areas. Farming doesn't need to plough and fertilize every square inch of Britain.'

'Fair enough,' I said non-committally. 'What areas are you using as unspoiled?'

'Ah!' said Bob, his eyes lighting up, 'Parsonage Down is a wonderful example. One of the very few areas of original down-land left in Southern England. Protected against damage from agriculture for all time, thank goodness, as it's now owned for conservation. You may not know the place, few people have been lucky enough to visit it. It's near Stonehenge in Wiltshire.'

A bell rang in my head. 'Do you mean Scotland Lodge,' I said, 'at Winterborne Stoke?'

'No, no. Parsonage Down,' said Bob, and he hurried on to tell me my part in the story. But clearly Parsonage Down and Scotland Lodge were the same place.

'Look,' I said, 'I do know the place you mean. I've known it more than thirty years. It's not original downland, it was all ploughed in the Napoleonic war. The down is as it is because of the way my Uncle Robert farmed it for fifty years.'

Bob looked at me with total incomprehension. He simply didn't understand a word I was trying to tell him.

'I see,' he said. 'Now, are you happy with the questions I want to ask?'

'No,' I said sadly but firmly. 'I'm not. Go and find someone else who'll give you the answers you want.'

And so he and the television crew left to finish the programme elsewhere leaving me and Uncle Robert to quiet obscurity.